Athlete: Jürgen Zäck
Race: 1995 Ironman-Europe

Personal Information

If found, please return. This almanac contains information considered vital to its owner.

Owner's name		
Winter	**Street**	
	City	
	State/province/ country	
	Phone/fax/e-mail	
Summer	**Street**	
	City	
	State/province/ country	
	Phone/fax/e-mail	
Best time and place to reach me		

	Equipment	Size	Brand
Swimming	Swimsuit		
	Goggles		
	Wetsuit		
Cycling	Shorts		
	Shirt		
	Helmet		
	Shoes		
Running	Shirt		
	Shorts		
	Warm-ups		
	Shoes		

Contents

Preface

This is the third edition of *The Total Triathlon Almanac*. The almanacs are the first complete training and racing companions for multisport athletes. Easy-to-carry, useful and flexible sources of personal training information, the almanacs have become de facto standards for triathletes and duathletes all over the world.

Feedback continues to come in, and—wanting to continuously improve the almanac—this feedback has been used as the basis for

the total triathlon almanac - 3

This almanac builds on previous editions, but is largely rewritten. The basic layout and design have been upgraded to reflect the wishes of the many triathletes who spoke up, while the weekly undated log pages have remained untouched. Table 1 shows how the emphasis has changed over the three editions.

Almanac Edition	Primary Focus	Secondary Focus
the total triathlon almanac - 1993	Static active stretching	Training and racing tips
the total triathlon almanac second edition	In-depth training and racing secrets from top professionals	Winter training Using a heart rate monitor
the total triathlon almanac - 3	Nutrition for performance Advanced heart rate monitor training and racing	In-depth training and racing secrets from top professionals

Table 1: Focus of the three editions of the total triathlon almanac

If you are interested in the training and racing information from our two earlier almanacs, you will find their tables of contents on page 160. If you cannot find them in your favorite sports or book store, there's an order form on page 163. In the United States, you can also call toll free 1-800-533-3644.

In this third edition, the almanac's format remains a series of separately contiguous right-hand and left-hand pages. The right-hand pages are weekly logs for you to keep. The left-hand pages comprise a training and racing guide full of tips by training authorities and expert athletes.

Date/Day	Swim	Bike	Run			Notes
Mo						
Tu						
We						
Th						
Fr						
Sa						
Su						
Weekly Goal						
Weekly Actual						
Year To Date						

THE RIGHT-HAND PAGES: 56-WEEK TRAINING LOG

Each right-hand page is an undated training log that covers one calendar week. Use it as you'd like, but remember: you train to get fitter and faster, not to have a meticulous logbook. The log can best help you monitor where you've been, where you are and where you're going if you keep your system simple.

Important: Check out the filled-in sample log (on page 129 in the appendix) for ideas on how to use the almanac. The design of the log page is intentionally open ended. You can personalize it to your desired level of detail; and this level of detail may change as the year progresses. In particular, with the almanac you don't have to carry the overhead of a fixed format for those weeks or months when your notation requirements are less comprehensive, such as during the off season.

THE LEFT-HAND PAGES: TRAINING INFORMATION

The left-hand pages contain a series of support material for the training and racing triathlete and duathlete. This material is organized into five sections: triathlon training fundamentals, nutrition for performance, heart rate monitor training, training secrets from the elite and designing your own schedule.

Triathlon Training Fundamentals

This chapter provides a structure for acquiring "triple fitness," and includes general training principles and guidelines. It is aimed at the beginning and intermediate triathlete or the recreational cross-trainer. There is one section for each of the three disciplines; each section is further divided into three phases, by fitness level. You will also find strength training guidelines, as well as exercise physiology definitions. (The appendix contains suggested training overviews, summarizing the training for each of the three phases, on page 130.)

Nutrition for Performance

In an attempt to respond to the most frequently asked questions by age-group triathletes, a chapter on nutrition for the active person is provided. This chapter is essentially written by Dr. Phil Maffetone, a chiropractor and applied kinesiologist with many years of experience in working with athletes, including Mark Allen and Mike Pigg.

Heart Rate Monitor Training

Working with several leading Swedish and Finnish authorities on exercise physiology and heart rate monitor training, I put together a concise chapter containing the basics for the second edition of the almanac. In this third edition, you will find the natural extension of that work: I went back to the Finns and asked Seppo Nuuttila (coach of some of Europe's best triathletes) and Pauli Kiuru for very specific details on how they train and use the monitor throughout the training and racing year. There is also a section on how some

Date/Day	Swim	Bike	Run			Notes
Mo						
Tu						
We						
Th						
Fr						
Sa						
Su						
Weekly Goal						
Weekly Actual						
Year To Date						

other leading professionals and age-group winners use the monitor.

Training Secrets from the Elite

This rewritten and updated chapter is aimed at the more accomplished triathlete, though most people find the information useful. The chapter comprehensively describes how some of the best in the field prepare for the triathlon season, and features even more specifics than before. In it, you'll find information on key workouts from our sport's leading stars for all parts of their training and racing year. The chapter on winter training from the second edition has been replaced with more in-depth training and racing advice, as well as how the best athletes taper and peak for short and long races.

Important: If you are a male age-group triathlete with hopes of winning your age-group or finishing in the top 100 in Hawaii (or anywhere else, for that matter), don't just look at how Mark Allen, Jeff Devlin or Pauli Kiuru train. You might be better off trying to emulate the training of Paula Newby-Fraser or Karen Smyers.

Designing Your Own Schedule

This new section provides a summary of what you need to think about when designing your own training schedule.

Appendix

The reorganized and rewritten appendix contains useful information for the training and racing year. You will find several planning and recording charts, as well as key workout templates, twelve pages with extra room for your own notes and four annual calendars. The appendix includes

• How to personalize your almanac log page

• Training
  - overviews
  - interval running and pacing
  - intervals with a heart rate monitor

• Interval training

• Strength training

• Annual training summary

• Goal setting, race planning and race results

• Notes

• Annual calendars (1996 through 1999)

Triathlon Training Fundamentals

Athlete: Mark Allen, USA
Race: 1995 Hawaii Ironman

At the finish line with Julie and Mats: "Dad, I've been waiting *all day* for you! Can we play now?"

◄─────────────────────────────────

This section can be used as a training and preparation guide for anyone interested in reaching and maintaining above-average fitness. Before you begin to train, however, it is advisable that you heed the warning from the American College of Sports Medicine:

> At or above 35 years of age, it is necessary for individuals to have a medical examination and a maximal exercise test before beginning a vigorous exercise program. At any age, the information gathered from an exercise test may be useful to establish an effective and safe exercise prescription. Maximal testing done for men at age 40 or above or women age 50 and older, even when no symptoms or risk factors are present, should be performed with physician supervision.

Further prerequisites are that, *regardless of your age*

• You be in good cardiovascular condition relative to the population and for your age

• You be familiar with your body's signals and able to differentiate between a simple muscular ache or pain (caused by a hard training effort) and the more serious pain caused by a sprained or a strained muscle, tendon or ligament

• You get a thorough physical exam and obtain a physician's release

TRAINING PHASES

The program is divided into three phases: adapting to regular training, structuring your workouts by length and intensity, and integrating more advanced intervals.

Phase One: Training Adaptation

Get mentally and physically used to a training regimen. Your mind, muscles, joints and tendons need time to adapt. This phase lasts one month to one year, depending on your goals and your fitness at the start.

Phase Two: Structure

Start structuring your training into hard, easy and long-distance days. *Listen to your body!* This phase lasts six weeks to six months.

Date/Day	Swim	Bike	Run			Notes
Mo						
Tu						
We						
Th						
Fr						
Sa						
Su						
Weekly Goal						
Weekly Actual						
Year To Date						

Phase Three: Intervals and Integration

Introduce more advanced speed and interval sessions, further improve your skills and prepare yourself for your first foot race or triathlon. By applying cross-training techniques, you will begin to integrate the three triathlon disciplines.

TRAINING PRINCIPLES AND GUIDELINES

This section summarizes the most important truths and pieces of wisdom about triathlon training. They have been rewritten and expanded from the previous almanacs.

1. Evaluate your present fitness level and set a realistic initial goal. Have a health-care professional knowledgeable in sports OK your proposed program.

2. Record your efforts. Keep a training diary or daily log, such as the one included in this almanac.

3. Performance = Stress + Rest. To achieve your maximal performance, you need to maximize all the parts of the equation. Doing so requires sensible and innovative training, as well as very serious rest. To learn when your body needs either exercise or rest is to learn how to train. Therefore, it is critical that you listen to what your body is telling you at all times. If you are tired, rest, don't train!

Learn to distinguish between the muscle discomfort that results from hard exercise and the more serious pain in joints, tendons and ligaments that may later result in injury, if unheeded. To decrease the risk of injury, develop and follow a hard/easy schedule. This means, for instance, that you *never* do hard or long training on two consecutive days.

4. Remember that training stresses your system. The exercise cycle is stress-rest-stress. Your system reacts to the stress, recovers and gets stronger during the rest, and is then ready for more stress. Each of us can stand different loads and needs different amounts of time to adapt. *You are an experiment of one.* Establish your own schedule; do not follow anyone else's. Listen to your body!

5. Be heart smart. Learn how to take your pulse or heart rate (on the side of your neck just below your jawline or on your wrist). Also, consider buying a heart rate monitor. The effects of training are monitored by time, distance and intensity. Although it is possible to gauge intensity by perceived effort, there is a direct correlation between intensity and heart rate. Not only is this measure more accurate than your perceived effort, it is easier to record, compile and analyze. (Go to page 70 for more information on training with a heart rate monitor.)

Date/Day	Swim	Bike	Run		Notes
Mo					
Tu					
We					
Th					
Fr					
Sa					
Su					
Weekly Goal					
Weekly Actual					
Year To Date					

6. Record your morning heart rate. Upon wakening and while still in bed, take your pulse. As your fitness improves, your morning resting heart rate will drop. If you have a heart rate of five to ten (or more) beats per minute (BPM) higher than your morning norm, you have not recovered from your previous day's exercising or whatever long- or short-term stress you've exposed your body to—including anxiety, lack of sleep and extended travel. You may also be catching a cold or fighting off some other illness. Be safe, take the day off.

7. Weigh regularly. If you are overweight, you may not lose much weight initially—but soon you should lose up to half a kg (one pound) per week. The "full body" aerobic exercises that comprise the triathlon consume no more than 1,000 kilocalories (kcal) per hour. The bigger you are, the more calories you consume. There are approximately 7,000 kcal per kg of fat (3,500 per pound).

8. Train on an empty stomach. Train at least three hours after your last meal. Exercising causes increased peristalsis, and for some, even cramps or diarrhea. A bowel movement before training or racing may prevent these abdominal symptoms.

9. Stay well-hydrated before, during and after training. A good rule of thumb is to drink as much as your stomach can handle every 20 minutes or so. Most people tolerate water best, particularly in hot temperatures. In hot and humid weather, drink more! There are also many sports drinks, carbohydrate gels and energy bars on the market, some better than others—experiment with them in training before using them in a race.

10. Eat as soon as you can after training. Exercise depletes you of important nutrients, water and calories. Replenish them as close to your training and racing effort as possible.

11. Wear the right clothes. In cold weather, wear several thin layers of clothing to protect against the wind and wet. In hot weather, wear light-colored clothes, ultraviolet (UV) protective eye shades and a visor or cap.

12. Use sunscreen. Wear a waterproof sunscreen if you go out in the sun, preferably one with a sun protection factor (SPF) of 15 or more. Look for a "broad spectrum" sunscreen with two or more UV absorbing ingredients.

13. "Bellybreathe." Bellybreathing requires practice, and you should do it deliberately just prior to training or racing. Take air into your belly and exhale against a slight resistance. This helps prevent getting a "stitch" while you exercise.

14. Warm up and warm down. Gradually warm up at the beginning of each session to decrease the risk of injury. Warm down at the end of each session to help speed recovery

Date/Day	Swim	Bike	Run			Notes
Mo						
Tu						
We						
Th						
Fr						
Sa						
Su						
Weekly Goal						
Weekly Actual						
Year To Date						

and prepare for your next workout, even if it's a day or two away. One of the effects of intense training is elevated levels of *lactic acid* in your system, which causes fatigue. The heavier the exercise, the more lactic acid is accumulated and the more important is a longer warm-down to help dissipate the lactic acid.

15. Go easy until you catch your second wind. It takes about five to ten minutes and a one-degree rise in body temperature to shunt the blood to the working muscles. When this happens you will begin to sweat lightly and your breathing will be easier—this is your second wind.

16. Stretch vigorously only after a workout. Before exercising, do only very light stretching, if any; start out very easily for five to ten minutes, stop to stretch if you like, and then resume your training.

The University of California, Berkeley Wellness Letter advises: "Don't bounce when stretching, since this actually tightens muscles. The best kind of stretch is the 'static' stretch, where you gradually increase the stretch without straining the muscles. Although recent studies have failed to show that stretching after a too strenuous workout heads off muscle soreness, it does promote flexibility and can keep your muscles from tightening up quickly." If you are interested in a complete performance stretching program, as used by Mark Allen, Paula Newby-Fraser and others, try static active stretching. A complete program can be found in the total triathlon almanac–1993 or the total runner's almanac. This program provides both stretching and trunk strengthening exercises.

17. Learn to read your body. Be aware of overtraining signs. If the second wind brings a cold, clammy sweat, head for home. Be alert to impending trouble. Loss of zest, light-headedness, scratchy throat, swollen glands, insomnia or palpitations are signs of trouble ahead.

18. Do not exercise when you have a cold. A cold indicates that you have some sort of infection in your body. You might be overtrained, overstressed or both. Wait a few days before you train again—take a nap during the time you would normally have spent at the gym, the pool or out on the road. On the other hand, many top athletes vigorously maintain that the key to avoiding a cold in the first place is to train daily. Though it has not been scientifically proven, they contend that exercise raises your body temperature and kills off the virus which would have caused the cold. In the Scandinavian countries and in Finland, people go to the sauna "to kill the kold." Also, since the common cold is caused by a virus, antibiotics will do no good.

19. Be alert for signs of injury. Most injuries result from too drastic a change in training. A change in shoes, an increase in weekly distance or intensity, hill work and so on are

Date/Day	Swim	Bike	Run			Notes
Mo						
Tu						
We						
Th						
Fr						
Sa						
Su						
Weekly Goal						
Weekly Actual						
Year To Date						

all factors that can increase your susceptibility to injury.

If you have a problem from running, there is almost always some associated weakness of the foot or a strength/flexibility imbalance. Or, one leg is shorter than the other. Use of heel lifts, arch supports, orthotics, shoe modifications and corrective exercises *(particularly stretching)* may be necessary.

20. If you get injured, back off. Go to a specialist in sports injuries (a good chiropractor, medical doctor or physical therapist). When you return to training, do not try to make up for lost time; your body won't accept it. Start up gradually!

21. Take advantage of your cross-training base. If you are injured, find a substitute for the activity that caused the injury.

22. When injured or in trouble, do what the San Francisco 49ers do, go to RICE. For minor strains, sprains and tendonitis, **R**est your injured part, **I**ce for a maximum of 15 minutes, **C**ompress (or support) by lightly wrapping a towel around the injury and then **E**levate the injured part above heart level. You can safely reapply ice every two to three hours for the first one to two days after these minor injuries. If your pain or injury is sharp, or persists for more than a few days, get professional advice.

23. Do not cheat on your sleep. Add an extra hour of sleep during heavy training periods. Take one or two naps, if possible.

24. Don't train right before you go to bed. Avoid strenuous exercise within a couple of hours of bedtime—it may "rev up" your system and make it hard to go to sleep.

25. Find compatible partners. Don't exercise with people who go substantially faster than you all the time. Every once in a while, such a "speed session" is good for you, but once a week is probably sufficient. A more prudent game plan to avoid injury or overtraining would be to train as part of a "speed group" one weekend and a "long distance group" the other, thus alternating between speed and distance.

One of the main sources of these guidelines is the fitness and running guru George A. Sheehan, M.D. (1918-1993), the author of Personal Best *and* Running to Win. *It is difficult to write about fitness and mention something he hasn't already addressed. An additional source is my wife, Dr. Sharon Svensson.*

Date/Day	Swim	Bike	Run			Notes
Mo						
Tu						
We						
Th						
Fr						
Sa						
Su						
Weekly Goal						
Weekly Actual						
Year To Date						

ANATOMY OF A TRAINING YEAR

Realizing that peak performance is not something you acquire in a few months or even a year, most successful triathletes adopt a multi-year plan. Not only is there a long list of specific skills you need to master, you also need to accumulate experience in putting them all together, in training and on race day.

You also have to give your body time to adapt to training over a longer period of time. As a consequence, endurance athletes have developed schedules, mostly annual, consisting of four main parts: the "off" season, base training, pre-competitive and competitive seasons. The chart that follows shows the relationships between volume, intensity and capacity during the four seasons.

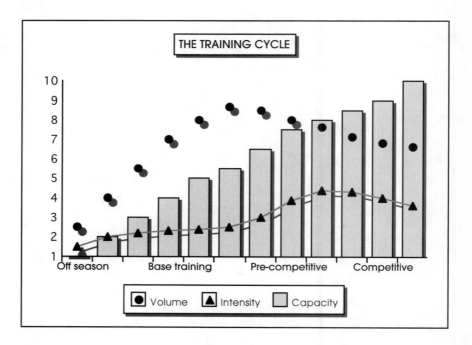

Your off season could be one or several months long. If you go through one of these cycles in a calendar year, your base training could be four to six months. And your pre-competitive season, when you start to incorporate serious interval sessions, could be two to three months; and your competitive season no more than three months.

Please note that many top triathletes start racing in the pre-competitive season, some even during base training. Others go through two of these cycles in a calendar year.

Date/Day	Swim	Bike	Run			Notes
Mo						
Tu						
We						
Th						
Fr						
Sa						
Su						
Weekly Goal						
Weekly Actual						
Year To Date						

Exercise Physiology Definitions

Resting heart rate (RHR): Your heart rate at complete rest, for example, before you get out of bed in the morning. The RHR can be decreased with training.

Lactic acid: A substance that accumulates in your system during exercise and causes fatigue. The heavier the exercise, the more lactic acid is accumulated. The term is often used synonymously with *lactates,* which is close enough (a lactate is a buffered lactic acid). A lactic acid blood level, molarity or concentration, of 2 mM (milli-moles per liter) is sometimes regarded as the aerobic threshold and 4 mM as the anaerobic threshold, though these values vary by individual.

Aerobic capacity level: The exercise intensity level at which your body's oxygen consumption is in balance with your metabolic waste products (lactic acid). Some researchers believe this is the minimum training level that will produce an endurance effect and they call it the aerobic threshold.

Anaerobic capacity level: Anaerobic threshold.

Anaerobic threshold (AT): The exercise intensity level after which any further increase in speed will cause a linear increase in lactic acid. Experts do not agree on the exact point at which the AT is reached. Still, you can improve your AT, and thus performance, with training. In the early season you may reach your AT at 140 BPM, mid-season at 150 BPM and late season at 160+ BPM, assuming you train properly. Some experts claim that the AT is a fixed value that can not be changed.

Maximum oxygen consumption (maximum oxygen uptake or VO$_2$max): A scientific value defined as the maximum amount of oxygen per minute of exercise that you are able to consume. This maximum rate is reached at a slower than maximum speed. (Your *anaerobic capacity* is what makes it possible for you to continue beyond this level. Then your body continues to supply energy even though the oxygen availability is inadequate and metabolic waste products are produced.) The VO$_2$max can be increased with training.

Maximum heart rate (MHR): The heart rate right before exhaustion at a maximum work load. The MHR cannot be increased with training. It decreases with age.

Copyright © 1996 by Tony Svensson

Date/Day	Swim	Bike	Run			Notes
Mo						
Tu						
We						
Th						
Fr						
Sa						
Su						
Weekly Goal						
Weekly Actual						
Year To Date						

SWIMMING

The advice and workouts described here are designed for the freestyle (Australian crawl) stroke, which provides the fastest propulsion through the water and is the most commonly used in triathlons.

Beginning and Intermediate Tips on Technique

It is virtually impossible to learn how to swim by reading a book. The basics have to be taught, drilled, retaught and drilled again. So your best bet is to have a swim coach or a friend work on your stroke and describe to you the concepts of *balance, catch, clean water, drag, hand entry, hands and feet as propelling surfaces, recovery, rotation, streamlining,* and so on. There are, however, some common faults in the freestyle stroke to watch out for:

1. Snaking. If you either over-reach as your hand enters the water in front of you and/or you *don't rotate enough,* you may be "snaking" through the water. (Snaking is a side-to-side wiggling motion that does very little to propel you forward.) This lack of trunk rotation also means that you have to rotate your entire head in order to breathe—it is more advantageous to let your hips do most of the rotation.

2. Low elbows. Your elbow should be higher than any other part of your arm or hand during the entire stroke. This technique will afford you more power and is often described as "high-elbow/low-hand pull and recovery."

3. Sloppy hand entry. Most freestyle stroke errors are from sloppy hand position during the breath. First, you need to relax your hand throughout the recovery. Then lead with your thumb as your hand enters the water in front of you, keeping your hand relaxed and fingers slightly apart (not clenched tightly together).

For more information on swimming technique, please go to the advanced tips section starting on page 30.

Phase One

Swim for 30 to 45 minutes, three times per week. Try to develop an even pace and get a feel for the rhythm of the freestyle stroke. Get used to the breathing pattern and practice bilateral breathing.

Phase Two

At this level, there are two general types of training: a) continuous swims lasting from 10 minutes to an hour; and b) shorter interval swims consisting of predetermined swim and rest periods. Two typical examples of interval sets follow:

- 10 by 100 at 1:45 on 2:15

- 5 by 200 at 3:45 on 4:30

Date/Day	Swim	Bike	Run			Notes
Mo						
Tu						
We						
Th						
Fr						
Sa						
Su						
Weekly Goal						
Weekly Actual						
Year To Date						

"At" indicates the total swim time; "on" is the swim plus rest time. In the first example, you swim 100 meters (if yards, deduct approximately 10 percent of your time) in one minute and 45 seconds, then take a 30-second rest period before starting again.

Phase Three

At this level, interval swim training is often differentiated into a) VO_2max sessions, which increase the oxygen carrying capacity of your system; and b) AT sessions, which improve your ability to work at a higher intensity for a longer period of time. (For more information on heart rate monitor training, please go to page 70.)

VO_2max Interval Training. During these swims, keep your heart rate at 80 to 95 percent of its maximum rate. Each repetition (rep) should be three to ten minutes of continuous work. In the recovery time, the heart rate should drop by 30 to 40 percent. Two examples of a VO_2max set for a 30-year-old who swims the 1,500 meter (~1,650 yard) freestyle in 22 minutes would be (in a 25-meter pool):

• 5 by 300 at 4:45 on 6:00

• 6 by 200 at 3:00 on 3:45

For this person, each rep should elevate the heart rate to about 170 BPM; each rest period should drop it to about 120 BPM.

AT Interval Training. AT training is not as intense as VO_2max, though the rest intervals are reduced significantly. Keep your heart rate at 75 to 90 percent of its max. The sets are 15 to 40 minutes long with rest periods of 15 to 40 seconds. Your heart rate should drop 10 to 15 percent during recovery. An example:

• 10 by 150 at 2:20 on 2:45

Distance Training. Distance training is simply swimming continuously for some period of time—from 15 minutes to several hours. The purpose is to develop a sense of stroke, rhythm and pace, and to learn how to maintain a pre-determined pace.

Include all three types of training every week. Your total weekly distance should range between 8,000 and 12,000 meters (or yards).

Open Water Swimming

The most important skill to master in open water is swimming straight. There is no line on the bottom of a lake or ocean so you must learn how to "sight" by raising your head out of the water. Open water swimming techniques in a triathlon differ from those used in pool swimming in two major ways:

Weekly Focus: *Month & Year:*

Date/Day	Swim	Bike	Run			Notes
Mo						
Tu						
We						
Th						
Fr						
Sa						
Su						
Weekly Goal						
Weekly Actual						
Year To Date						

- More body rotation (facilitates breathing in choppy water as well as puts less load on the arms and more on the stronger back and side muscles)

- Weaker kick (your kick is more for stabilization than for forward propulsion)

You will also notice the general anarchy surrounding a mass swim start. To minimize your risk of being hit or colliding with other swimmers, seed yourself. If you are not a strong swimmer, stand near the end.

Advanced Freestyle Tips

The sources for these more advanced hints and tips are the Stanford University head swim coaches Richard Quick and Skip Kenney (both are also head coaches of the 1996 US Olympic Teams), as well as their strength and technique coach, Ross Gerry. These gentlemen have coached numerous NCAA champion teams and Olympians. A selection of the advice they give their swimmers is compiled here.

1. Go faster. There are two ways you can increase your speed: a) by being stronger and fitter and b) by creating less resistance in the water. Guess which is better!

2. "Sidestroke" your freestyle. The freestyle is actually a side stroke (or "long-axis stroke"). The advantages of rotating along your longitudinal axis are that: a) you create less resistance by slicing through the water more efficiently, and b) you're able to also use the larger trunk muscles, which provide more power than your arm muscles alone. Again, this is particularly important in open water swims.

3. Rotate. If you find yourself swimming flat (most people do, particularly when they get tired), try the mantra "trunk rotation." If you have problems visualizing trunk rotation, think of yourself as a rotating skewer on a barbecue. Also, you use your pulling hand as an "anchor" to facilitate hip rotation. As your flexibility increases, you will be able to rotate better.

4. Keep your head still as you rotate. You have a big head. In fact, your head weighs as much as a racing bicycle! Whatever you do in the water with your head will drastically affect the rest of your body and thus your body alignment. And a body out of alignment creates more drag, as well as forces you to compensate, wasting energy that should be propelling you forward.

5. Swim tall. Increased flexibility and trunk rotation, which can both be improved with stretching exercises, allow you to swim taller. The taller you make yourself, the less resistance you create. Also, the taller you swim, the fewer strokes you have to take per lap. The fewer strokes you take per lap, while maintaining or increasing your speed, the better off you are. Good swimmers generate a tremendous amount of forward propulsion from

Date/Day	Swim	Bike	Run			Notes
Mo						
Tu						
We						
Th						
Fr						
Sa						
Su						
Weekly Goal						
Weekly Actual						
Year To Date						

each stroke, and spend a lot of time developing this skill.

6. Kick without a kickboard. Kick on your side for a while with one goggle out of the water, then rotate and kick on the other side. Your kicks should be small and fast. If you still don't have enough propulsion to make it to the other end of the pool without reaching your maximum heart rate, try the same drill with smaller, high speed fins, such as Zoomers™. When you rotate from side to side in this drill, you want a rapid and fluid transition, which is what freestyle (and backstroke) swimming is all about: *streamlined, rotation-intensive, forward motion.*

Realizing the limitations of the written word, it is recommended that you find a copy of the video *Swim Smarter—Swim Faster* by Richard Quick and Skip Kenney. It shows the four strokes (backstroke, breaststroke, butterfly and freestyle) and the drills used to refine them. If you really want to tear up the pool, try *Swim Smarter—Swim Faster II,* their video on starts and turns. Another excellent video is *Swim Power* by Steve Tarpinian.

CYCLING
The focus in this section is on preparing you for an individual time trial where you must run a foot race directly after getting off the bike.

Equipment
A racing bike is very light (sometimes as low as 8 kg), generally with a steel frame and aluminum components. More exotic materials include aluminum, magnesium, titanium and graphite composites. The price ranges from $400 to well over $4,000.

Aside from a bicycle, you need a helmet, cleated shoes, shorts with padding in the crotch and perhaps gloves. Later you can invest in other useful items that can make your riding both more enjoyable and faster. Examples are a cycling jersey with pockets, aerodynamic handlebars with armrests, special wheels with fewer and aerodynamic spokes to use in races, or a custom built frame.

Technique and Position
Except for climbing steep hills and sprinting, sit on your bike with your torso leaning forward; try to relax your upper body. This forward leaning posture is aerodynamically efficient. If you sit up straight or let your arms stick out, you'll catch the wind and slow down. Think of yourself as a Ferrari in a wind tunnel. When you ride standing up, place your hands on the brake hoods (assuming you have conventional handle bars) and rock your bike from side to side. This affords you more efficiency and power.

Pedaling and Shifting Gears
If you use your gears properly, you can ride more swiftly and efficiently. Between 75 and

Weekly Focus: *Month & Year:*

Date/Day	Swim	Bike	Run			Notes
Mo						
Tu						
We						
Th						
Fr						
Sa						
Su						
Weekly Goal						
Weekly Actual						
Year To Date						

90 rotations per minute (RPM) is common for a triathlete in a time trial, but a cyclist in a pack often spins from 80 to 110+ RPM. Try to pedal in circles. Push down between one and five o'clock; pull up (without jerking) from seven to eleven. Your objective is to make the entire revolution perfectly smooth. Think circles. Think flow. Think efficiency.

When choosing gears, follow these guidelines: The big chain ring is the normal position of the front derailleur. The freewheel is usually in one of the four middle gears. As you approach a hill, estimate the steepness of the climb, choose the right gear on your free-wheel and shift to the small chain ring as appropriate. Fine-tune with your rear derailleur, if necessary. To facilitate shifting, decrease the pedal pressure as you shift.

Phase One

To get your body used to the bicycle and to cycling, ride every other day, starting out with 30 minutes to an hour; take a longer ride of less than two hours on weekends. Your entire body may ache, particularly your hands, neck, back and quadriceps. Your private parts and rear end will also experience a new kind of distress. One way to minimize the friction on your skin is to apply a thick lotion to your sitting area before every ride.

Phase Two

Now you'll start differentiating your training. If you ride three times a week, take one hard ride, one easy ride and one long ride. The hard ride might be for 45 minutes at a fast pace, the easy ride might be for an hour and the long ride for two hours.

It is important to ride with a purpose. On your hard day, warm up for about 15 minutes; then start pushing the pace. Try to maintain the intensity despite your elevated pulse. On your easy day, focus on developing an even cadence and notice how *good* it feels to ride your bicycle. On your long day, attempt to keep a healthy clip throughout the ride. Near the end of your first two hour ride, you may enter a new dimension of awareness called "bonking." It's the cyclist's version of hitting the wall and, no fun: your system is depleted of available glycogen and your muscles are screaming for more. Welcome to the wonderful world of cycling!

Phase Three

It's time to differentiate your training further and ride longer distances. There are four components to becoming a better cyclist: speed, intensity, strength and endurance.

Speed. Speed is not directly proportional to how hard you ride; technique and relaxed efficiency are also involved. Choose a relatively flat road. Pedal until you are working hard, then slack off somewhat, relax your upper body and sense how efficient you are. Pedal in circles, keep your aerodynamic tuck and notice how the tires sing against the pavement as you move forward. Stay in your efficient work zone (your "efficiency win-dow"). Physiologically, this type of training is near your aerobic threshold, i.e., approxi-

Date/Day	Swim	Bike	Run			Notes
Mo						
Tu						
We						
Th						
Fr						
Sa						
Su						
Weekly Goal						
Weekly Actual						
Year To Date						

mately 35 to 45 BPM below your maximum heart rate. You want to avoid oxygen debt.

Intensity. Intensity training is harder than speed training; it is often the level you would use in a longer race. Try to reach a steady state where you venture out of your efficiency window; in fact, try to move your efficiency window upwards. Maintain the pace even if you experience some oxygen debt and lactic acid buildup. Try to cycle "through" small inclines by standing up, but shift if your pedaling cadence drops. Physiologically, intensity training is closer to your AT, i.e., approximately 20 to 30 BPM below your maximum heart rate.

Strength. The best strength training comes from intervals, hill riding or "fartlek." For intervals, you can ride 2,000 meters (or one-milers) in two to four minutes, with a working pulse no more than 5 to 10 BPM above your AT. Let your pulse slow to approximately 60 percent of your max before the next interval. Aim for a total of five to ten repetitions, all at the same speed. Alternatively, try riding with one or more riders in a pace line. Pull for one to three minutes at a high pace, then go back to the end of the pace line and draft.

Hill training is the best strength training you can do—but to benefit from it safely and avoid the risk of knee injury, you must be in good shape. Obviously, you also need hills. In phase three, a long hill climb should last from 30 to 60 minutes. You can climb hills sitting down or standing up; in general, a lighter cyclist spends more time standing up than does a heavier one.

Fartlek (a Swedish word meaning "speed play") is unstructured intervals of different length and intensity. You can chase a friend for fun, or sprint to the next road sign.

Endurance. Ride continuously for several hours at a healthy clip—don't ride too slowly or so fast that you go anaerobic. At this stage, your long rides should be three hours, or more. It is important to stay efficient throughout the ride at a pace you can maintain. Think "comfortable efficiency"; and remember to eat and drink well to avoid bonking.

The Social Ride. Though not strictly a component you train for, the social ride has its place in your arsenal. Not only is this ride good for your mental health, but also important for your body's recovery. Even Ironman winners are serious about their easy spin rides and make them part of their regular training or social life.

Date/Day	Swim	Bike	Run			Notes
Mo						
Tu						
We						
Th						
Fr						
Sa						
Su						
Weekly Goal						
Weekly Actual						
Year To Date						

RUNNING

Running is the least complicated of the three triathlon disciplines, since it can be done virtually anywhere. It is also the most difficult to excel in, particularly in triathlons, where you begin your run already fatigued.

Principles and Guidelines: Running

1. Remember, *Performance = Stress + Rest*. Running is hard on your body. Unless you're an accomplished runner to begin with, never run on two consecutive days until you reach the third phase. Even then, never run hard or long on two consecutive days.

2. Do not increase your total weekly distance more than 10 percent per week.

Equipment

Buy a top quality brand name shoes (and there's about a dozen of those). Go to a running store staffed by runners and tell them you want a good shoe. They will ask you what kind of running you do (distance, surface, etc.) and analyze the characteristics of your gait (pronation, supination, heel striker, fore foot striker, and so on). The shoes you buy should fit "like a glove" and give you the support your feet need based on your gait. They should be long enough to allow one thumb's width from your longest toe to the end of the shoe. Aside from excellent shoes, the props needed for running are minimal.

Phase One

Running places considerable stress on your body, so it's important to give your muscles and joints time to adapt. Start out slowly; don't do too much, too soon! First, you must *enjoy* the experience. It is very hard to stick to a regular program that makes you miserable. Second, give yourself an incentive by setting a goal (remember, a realistic goal). Select a 5 to 10 km (10 km = 6.22 miles) foot race six weeks to six months down the road and develop a training plan for it.

Start training by going out for 30 to 45 minutes two or three times per week. Separate your runs by at least one day of rest. Go out for a predetermined time, not a distance. Jog a little, then walk a little at first, if you need to. Stay within your comfort zone. Find a pace at which you can carry on a conversation. Don't push too hard; you won't enjoy yourself, and you may become injured.

Your Running Form. At this point, don't worry about form—just relax and do what comes naturally. Every runner has an individual style that's as unique as his or her personality. Drop your shoulders and swing your arms loosely with your fingers relaxed. Look around, enjoy the day and let your mind wander for a while. Then return to the task at hand and notice how your body feels.

After three to six weeks, include some hills, but again, don't push too hard. Pace yourself

Date/Day	Swim	Bike	Run			Notes
Mo						
Tu						
We						
Th						
Fr						
Sa						
Su						
Weekly Goal						
Weekly Actual						
Year To Date						

and take the downhills easy. Listen to your body.

Phase Two

Your objectives are to develop speed, strength and endurance. This involves three types of workouts; you will do each one once a week. You may also add one more day of running. For example, one of your rest days may now become a short, easy run, to avoid two consecutive hard workouts.

Leg Speed. The fartlek workout was created to develop leg speed. After a five- to ten-minute warm-up, increase the pace for a short time, then jog again. Fartlek is unstructured: just run according to how you feel and for no longer than 45 minutes.

Strength. The "tempo run" develops strength. This hard, steady run should cover three to five kilometers, at a pace that you can maintain for that distance and that increases your heart rate. Another type of strength workout is a hilly run at a brisk pace. As you approach a hill, get up on your toes and lift your knees. Push your arms down and back and pump yourself up the hill. Run the downhill stretches with short, quick steps. Your hips should lean forward and your body float down the hill.

Endurance. The LSD (long, slow distance or long, steady distance) run develops endurance. It should be approximately twice as long as your average run. Most people save the LSD run for the weekend.

Remember, never run any of these three workouts on consecutive days. You need that easy day in-between to recover.

Your Running Form. As you increase the intensity of your workouts, start monitoring your running style and try to become more efficient. Look ahead about five meters. Relax your facial muscles and jaw; drop your shoulders. Swing your arms loosely at your sides and avoid crossing them over the body's centerline (this wastes energy). Hands are cupped and relaxed (not clenched). All motion is forward, everything else is relaxed. Visualize the form of a good runner you admire and mimic that form. For long-distance running, a shorter, quicker, almost shuffling type of step is more efficient and less stressful. It is good form to land on the outside of the heel, roll inward and push off with the big toe. Changing your running form takes time. Be patient.

Phase Three

It is now time to incorporate sessions focusing on running at a harder-than-race pace for shorter intervals. When you first introduce intervals, decrease your weekly distance by about 10 percent so your body can adapt to the new stress—do only one interval workout per week. Interval running increases your leg speed, strengthens your heart muscle and teaches you to run fast when your body is already tired. The interval charts in the appen-

Date/Day	Swim	Bike	Run			Notes
Mo						
Tu						
We						
Th						
Fr						
Sa						
Su						
Weekly Goal						
Weekly Actual						
Year To Date						

dix outline your interval sessions in more detail. Each interval should elevate your heart rate to near, or slightly above, your AT.

This would translate to approximately 85 percent of max during each fast run. Then let it drop to 60 percent of max before starting to run again. You want to finish each run evenly and in control, but you obviously don't want too much rest.

If possible, use a track. During these sessions, warm up by running slowly for about 15 minutes; then run 3 by 2,000 m—or three to four one-milers—and walk one lap of the track for recovery between each interval. Then warm down 15 to 30 minutes.

To prepare for shorter races, run two laps (= 800 m, 880 yards or half a mile) at the same pace you expect to run on race day, then walk half a lap. For instance, 10 km at 43:30 comes out to a km pace of 4:21 (or a mile pace of 7:00). Gradually work up to five of these intervals all run at the same pace. Then run 2,000 m—or one mile—for time.

Intervals as Confidence Builders. Intervals should not wipe you out. It is only a preliminary test, not the final exam. You should leave the track feeling pleased to have challenged yourself and confident that you could do more if you had to. After only a few interval sessions, you will run more comfortably and efficiently at a quicker pace and be able to run faster while fatigued. This, in turn, will do wonders for your confidence; and confidence is the essence of racing well.

Date/Day	Swim	Bike	Run			Notes
Mo						
Tu						
We						
Th						
Fr						
Sa						
Su						
Weekly Goal						
Weekly Actual						
Year To Date						

Strength Training

Why?

Strength training is not only for building bulk. Research in physiology clearly shows that strength training is essential for optimum endurance and performance. It is also well documented that we lose muscle mass during prolonged non-resistance exercise, such as running. We also lose more muscle mass as we get older.

Equipment

Most people who go to the weight room for the first time are more comfortable using the resistance machines than the free weights. There are advantages and disadvantages to each. Machines are generally safer and require less skill to operate; they also provide a very specific and predetermined range of motion for one or several muscle groups. Some machines are designed to load the muscle more evenly throughout its entire range of motion for a better, or different, training effect.

Free weights are simpler. It's just you, the weight and gravity. But, unless you know what you're doing, free weights can be dangerous. Dropping a dumbbell or a plate on your toe, even a light one, is not a pleasant experience. However, free weights add important elements of balance and coordination to your exercise, among other things. Again, talk to your trainer or the gym staff about how best to use them.

The following is a list of strength training tips and common "gym customs." Ideally, they are combined with the training guidelines, starting on page 14. You will also find strength training templates in the appendix, starting on page 139.

1. Start out easily. Just because the woman half your size bench presses two big plates, it doesn't mean you can. The first week or so, be content with bench pressing the bar alone and use very tiny weights throughout your program. Also, if you have been away from the gym for more than a week, start out with considerably less weight than when you left off.

2. Beware of the lure of the heavy weight. Lifting weights that are too heavy will cause you to strain, lose form and *decrease* the training effect. Even after you get used to weight training, increase your weights gradually over time.

3. Work your entire body. You need to develop a program that exercises all major muscle groups. Don't just focus on your arms and legs; remember that your trunk, or *core,* (abdominal, side, upper and lower back muscles) is just as important in the triathlon. The core exercises provide critical stability to the skeleton where the muscles of the extremities attach.

4. Find an instructor and/or a partner. If you are unfamiliar with the equipment in the gym or you have limited knowledge about anatomy or strength training, it is best to seek out a trainer. Most gyms have certified strength instructors who can show you exactly which equipment to use, as well as how and why. After only a few sessions, you should be able to train on your own, or with a partner.

Date/Day	Swim	Bike	Run			Notes
Mo						
Tu						
We						
Th						
Fr						
Sa						
Su						
Weekly Goal						
Weekly Actual						
Year To Date						

Strength Training, *continued*

5. Find a spotter. When lifting heavy weights, such as with the bench press or squats, always have somebody watch you. The spotter is there to assist you, if necessary. If you don't have a partner, just courteously ask somebody to spot you for a minute. The person you ask will gladly help you and even provide needed encouragement to finish those last reps when the going gets tough, particularly if you are wearing a triathlon finisher's shirt.

6. Don't hold your breath. Some people follow a breathing pattern when lifting weights—such as exhaling on exertion—others don't. Just never hold your breath, as this will limit your oxygen supply and may cause you to faint—even if you're a big boy.

7. Wear a weight lifting belt. Protect and stabilize your lower back and torso by wearing a weight lifting belt during demanding exercises such as squats. The best ones are made of leather.

8. Follow the rules. Never leave plates on the bar or dumbbells on the floor when you are finished, even if that's where you found them. Always put the weights (bars, barbells, dumbbells and plates) back in their racks. Also, follow the rules of the club. Each club has a set of safety and courtesy guidelines that you must follow—remember, there's almost *always* somebody bigger than you at the gym!

9. Load and stack plates properly. Plates have one side with the weight stamped on it (the face), and one side blank. You load the bar with the plate face in; you stack the plate back on the rack face out.

10. Alternate exercises. If you go to the gym specifically to "build" muscle mass—say in the off-season—you need to alternate exercises. One day you focus on the upper body, the next on the lower body. During the season, strength training is only a complement to your other training, then going to the gym two to four times a week is sufficient.

Important: If you are interested in a detailed strength training program designed specifically for triathletes and other endurance athletes, try the video *Strength Training for Total Body Fitness* featuring Ironman champions Mark Allen and Paula Newby-Fraser with certified fitness specialist Diane Buchta. There is an order form on page 163.

Helping out with these guidelines, as well as the swimming chapter, was Ross Gerry, the assistant women's swim coach at Stanford University. Ross has a Master of Education from Boston University, with a specialty in human movement. He is a certified strength and conditioning specialist (CSCS) from the National Strength and Conditioning Association (NSCA). He also coaches the Stanford Masters swim team, where, particularly his contingent of triathletes, test his vast knowledge, immeasurable patience and good sense of humor every day.

Nutrition for Performance

Athlete: Paula Newby-Fraser, Zimbabwe
Race: 1995 Ironman-Europe

Fueling up about one hour into the bike ride

◄——————————————————

Most athletes seeking to improve performance look at the latest high-tech equipment or think about changing their training routines, for instance, by adding more miles or more sprints. But an important way to make a significant improvement in performance can be as close as the kitchen table: what you eat and drink can affect how you perform. You are what you eat. In order of importance, here is what your body requires:

1. Water: more than 60 percent of your body weight and a full 85 percent of your muscles. Basic to all life, water is your body's essential lubricant and plays a critical role in regulating your temperature and flushing out waste products, among other things. So training without an ample supply of water before, during and after is bad news, indeed. During heavy exercising, your water requirements increase 10 to 15 times.

2. Macronutrients: carbohydrates, fats and protein. You need a lot of these. They provide energy and are the building blocks your body uses to repair and renew itself. Carbohydrates are made up of glucose, fats are composed of fatty acids and proteins consist of amino acids.

3. Micronutrients: vitamins, minerals and enzymes. Though micronutrients are essential for life, you need them in much smaller amounts. They are like spices in cooking: essential to enhance the recipe, but only in moderate quantities. Large amounts may spoil the dish.

GUIDELINES AND RECOMMENDATIONS

The following is a list of 10 guidelines, based partly on the actual practices of athletes (and the nutritional authorities who work with them, particularly Dr. Philip Maffetone) and partly on publications from the National Academy of Sciences, the National Institute of Health and the American Heart Association.

1. Balance your diet. Eat a diet consisting largely of complex carbohydrates, but don't cut

Date/Day	Swim	Bike	Run			Notes
Mo						
Tu						
We						
Th						
Fr						
Sa						
Su						
Weekly Goal						
Weekly Actual						
Year To Date						

out all fats and proteins. Approximate percentages of caloric intake are listed in Table 2.

Carbohydrates	Fats	Protein
50-60%	20-30%	20-30%

Table 2: A common diet for the active person

Some endurance athletes maintain a diet consisting of 40 percent carbohydrates, 30 percent fats and 30 percent protein with great success. Dr. Maffetone, and many of the athletes he works with, are proponents of the 40-30-30 diet, but he also states: "I've never found a magic formula. You may have needs that demand a 50-25-25 diet, while other athletes will best operate on a 60-20-20 diet. The key to finding your optimal diet is just that—find it."

2. Look for complex carbohydrates first. A common "healthy diet" consists primarily of green leafy vegetables and starchy vegetables, grains, fruits, some dairy products and fish or poultry. Some triathletes—Mark Allen among others—believe in eating red meat several times a week during the heaviest phases of training and racing.

3. Limit your intake of saturated fats. Some fats are good and others are not; saturated fats contribute to high blood cholesterol levels. Most unsaturated ("good") fats are liquid at room temperature, while saturated fats are not.

4. Get your protein from low-fat sources. Seafood, poultry, lean meats and eggs—yes, eggs—are excellent sources of animal protein. The list of non-animal protein sources is long. It includes beans, peas, nuts and seeds, though the latter two can be high in fats.

5. Avoid too much sugar. Many foods high in sugar are also high in fat, and sugar promotes tooth decay. Though virtually fat free, the many energy drinks on the market are loaded with sugars. Drink them only in conjunction with exercise; otherwise drink water.

Dr. Maffetone comments, "I feel strongly about saying that it's the refined sugar in our diet that causes so many health and fitness problems. Excess insulin production is an important factor since it may inhibit endurance. I always say 'avoid sugar and sugar-containing foods as much as possible.'"

6. Limit your intake of dietary cholesterol. Since your body produces most of the cholesterol it needs in your bloodstream, you should limit your daily intake to 300 mg. On the other hand, Dr. Maffetone maintains that "The body only absorbs 2 to 4 mg of cholesterol per kg of body weight. And most people can eat much more than 300 mg of cholesterol per day without elevating their blood cholesterol. Some wonderfully nutritious

Date/Day	Swim	Bike	Run			Notes
Mo						
Tu						
We						
Th						
Fr						
Sa						
Su						
Weekly Goal						
Weekly Actual						
Year To Date						

foods (such as eggs) are avoided because they contain supposedly too much cholesterol."

7. Make your own decision about vitamins. Vitamin supplementation may be the most controversial topic of all—some health authorities recommend against it—still, many athletes take extra vitamins. So, if you like, supplement your diet with vitamins and minerals. Multivitamins, calcium, iron and vitamin C are among the most popular. But beware of overdosing on vitamins A and D, in particular.

8. Eat intelligently throughout the day. Eat a good, high-protein breakfast, then a light lunch. Save the carbohydrates for the meal after the workout to replenish muscle sugar. Try to replace lost calories as soon after you exercise as possible. Eat several small meals rather than one or two large ones.

9. Avoid processed foods. The fresher the food, the better. If people have tinkered with it, it's probably not as healthy as it was directly from the tree, plant or stream. If food comes in a natural wrapping, as a banana does, you can almost never go wrong. The second best is frozen food. A distant third is dried, vacuum packed or canned.

10. Hydrate well. Drink water as often as you can. When you feel hungry or "anxious for something," the feeling may be just a sign of dehydration. Try a glass of water first. Then, if that doesn't do it, eat something.

WATER: THE MOST IMPORTANT NUTRIENT
Most of the liquid your body requires is obtained by water intake (about 10 percent is produced by our cells during metabolism—converting carbohydrates and fats to energy). Normally, about two-thirds of our supply comes from drinking fluids (mostly water) and one-third from foods.

Water Loss and Exercise
In most endurance events, the majority of competitors finish the race dehydrated. Unfortunately, too many of them also *start* the race that way. In a two-hour endurance event, for example, water loss—dehydration—may reduce the body's water content by up to 10 percent, despite efforts to drink enough water. This is a significant and dangerous situation that affects both your health and your performance.

Water input must balance normal water loss, both at rest and during exercise. Water loss occurs through several bodily processes:

Skin Evaporation. Evaporation of water from the skin is important to control body temperature. Even under cool, resting conditions, about 30 percent of our water loss occurs in this way. But during endurance activity, sweating increases this loss dramatically—

Date/Day	Swim	Bike	Run			Notes
Mo						
Tu						
We						
Th						
Fr						
Sa						
Su						
Weekly Goal						
Weekly Actual						
Year To Date						

about 300 times. The amount is determined partly by the temperature of the air (the higher the temperature, the more water loss) and body size (the larger the person, the more water loss).

Exhalation. Water lost in exhaled air is also significant. The air going into and out of our lungs needs to be humidified. Because of our increased breathing rate during exercise, this water loss is increased five to ten times.

Digestion. During rest, most water is lost through the kidneys. This water is used to help eliminate waste products from the body. Also, a small but significant amount of water (about five percent) is lost through the intestine. During exercise, the body attempts to conserve water, and loss through the kidneys is very limited—50 to 70 times less than at rest. There is normally no water loss from the intestine when exercising.

Water Loss and Blood Volume
One of the main problems with dehydration is that it decreases blood volume. Maintaining blood volume is important because so many vital functions rely on the blood to

- Carry oxygen to the muscles

- Transport nutrients, including glucose, fats and amino acids

- Remove carbon dioxide and other waste products

- Neutralize lactic acid to maintain a proper pH balance

- Remove excess heat generated during exercise

- Help maintain efficient cardiovascular function

- Transport hormones that regulate muscular activity during exercise and aid in recovery

Water Loss during Competition
Even a small water loss reduces your performance potential. Studies show that an athlete who can run a 10,000 meter race in 35 minutes when normally hydrated, takes almost 38 minutes when dehydrated by four percent. The peak performance of athletes who are well-hydrated diminishes by 10 percent when they are only two percent dehydrated—if they are five percent dehydrated, the performance diminishes by 30 percent. This latter example can mean an extra three hours, or more, in an Ironman race. In fact, in races such as the Hawaii Ironman, the average person can lose as much as two liters of water per hour!

Dehydration also causes a higher heart rate; four hours of training without water may cause the heart rate to increase by 30 beats a minute.

Date/Day	Swim	Bike	Run			Notes
Mo						
Tu						
We						
Th						
Fr						
Sa						
Su						
Weekly Goal						
Weekly Actual						
Year To Date						

Your sensation of thirst, regulated by the area of the brain called the *hypothalamus,* is a response to a lower concentration of water in the blood. Therefore, thirst is a delayed response and not a real-time indication of your actual water need. In other words, when you feel thirsty, you're already dehydrated. Unfortunately, the human body does not function like that of many other animals, who, by drinking enough water, can consume 10 percent of their total body weight within the first few minutes after heavy exercise. We humans need to drink water in small amounts much more frequently.

The best way to regulate water levels is to drink plain water all day long. Avoid carbonated water, which may cause intestinal distress. And during training and competition, the same is true; drinking smaller amounts on a regular basis throughout the activity is the best way to stay as hydrated as possible.

Even so, most competitors will cross the finish line dehydrated to some degree. In addition to not being able to replenish water fast enough, most athletes physically cannot consume enough water. Forcing water beyond your ability will only result in stomach bloating (from swallowing air) or nausea.

During endurance events, liquids containing carbohydrates and sodium are of great value. But you should drink these fluids in addition to, not instead of, plain water. Carbohydrates provide immediate energy and help you maintain the burning of fats—your most important endurance fuel.

Dehydration, however, involves more than just water deficiency. As the intensity and duration of exercise increase, the sweating rate also increases, and sodium loss is accelerated (with minimal losses of potassium). Low blood sodium, called *hyponatremia,* can result in general weakness and disorientation, and, in extreme cases, seizures and coma. In long events, too much water intake without sodium may aggravate sodium deficiency. That's why many sports drinks contain sodium.

Heat Illness
Since the body dissipates heat with the help of water, the risk of heat illness accompanies dehydration and sodium loss. Even short races in hot weather can cause heat illness. It has three stages: muscle cramps, exhaustion and heat stroke.

1. Muscle cramping. Cramping is a classic result of dehydration and/or sodium deficiency. It first attacks the larger, most often used muscles such as the hamstring and quadriceps group, and the calf muscles.

2. Exhaustion. Heat exhaustion is first signaled by excess fatigue, dizziness and shortness of breath. Later symptoms include vomiting and fainting. Dehydration causes the cardio-

Date/Day	Swim	Bike	Run			Notes
Mo						
Tu						
We						
Th						
Fr						
Sa						
Su						
Weekly Goal						
Weekly Actual						
Year To Date						

vascular system to become inefficient, diminishing blood flow to both the muscles and the skin. Hence, the muscles become nutrient-deficient and body heat accumulates.

3. Heat stroke. The third stage of heat illness is a life threatening disorder that requires immediate medical attention. The signs include a high core body temperature (sometimes above 40 °C), cessation of sweating, very rapid pulse and breathing, hot and dry skin, confusion and often unconsciousness. If unattended, heat stroke can progress to coma and death. First-aid treatment includes cooling the body with cold water or ice.

How to Prevent Dehydration

1. Don't wait for a race to hydrate. Drink water throughout the day, especially the week before an event. Drink smaller amounts all day rather than two or three large doses.

2. Have a water bottle near you at all times, and make drinking water a habit. In particular, keep water near you during work hours (at your desk, by the phone) or wherever else you spend your time.

3. Eat some sodium rich foods (vegetables, sea salt and soy sauce) regularly, especially during hot weather and the week before an event.

4. Get used to drinking water before, during and immediately after training. Simulate race conditions by drinking water during fast-paced workouts. Learn to drink without swallowing air. Remember that following heavy sweating, complete water replacement may take 24 to 48 hours.

5. Discover which drinks with carbohydrates and sodium you tolerate well and feel the best after consuming. Experiment during training rather than during a race.

MACRONUTRIENT RATIOS

There is no perfect diet. But you can achieve optimal use of the macronutrients by carefully determining just the right proportions of nutrients for your specific needs.

Most energy is derived from carbohydrates (glucose) and fats (fatty acids). Protein (amino acids) also provides energy, especially if carbohydrate and fat intake is inadequate. But the most abundant energy source from the diet is fat. One molecule of neutral fat yields about 460 molecules of adenosinetriphosphate (ATP). The same amount of glucose yields only 36 molecules of ATP. Fat stores in a healthy adult man offer 100,000 kcal of energy; glucose stores, called glycogen, offer only 2,000 kcal. Fat burning, which is essential for endurance over long distances, is often the missing ingredient in the training programs of even world class performers.

Date/Day	Swim	Bike	Run			Notes
Mo						
Tu						
We						
Th						
Fr						
Sa						
Su						
Weekly Goal						
Weekly Actual						
Year To Date						

In order to burn more fat, you need to eat enough of the proper fats, and you need to moderate your intake of carbohydrates. Burning the fat in your body is related to the source of energy used most—fat or sugar—as well as insulin levels, which are directly related to carbohydrate intake. So the ratio of macronutrients—the carbohydrates, proteins and fats—you take in is very important to how your body functions.

For most people (including athletes), a good starting ratio is about 40 percent carbohydrate, 30 percent protein and 30 percent fat. This is radically different from the 70 percent carbohydrate and low-fat diet often recommended today, particularly since a significant segment of the population (about a third to a half) is carbohydrate intolerant. (This condition is explained in the section on carbohydrates, later in this chapter.) For athletes in training, a diet with about 30 percent fats is effective. Again, the key to finding your own optimal diet is just that—find it.

Calculating Macronutrient Ratios

Here's how to calculate the ratio of macronutrients from the calories of the foods you are eating: Multiply the number of grams of each kind of food by 4 for carbohydrates, 4 for proteins and 9 for fats. For example, if a certain meal contains 190 calories, with 19 grams of carbohydrates, to determine the percentage of carbohydrates, multiply the 19 grams by 4, which equals 76. Then divide 76 by 190 (total calories in the meal), which equals 0.40 or 40 percent. (If you don't want to bother counting calories and grams and practicing your math, take a look at a day's sample menu offered below. It provides a healthy ratio for most people.)

Sample 40-30-30 meals

Breakfast: 8 oz. (~240 ml) tomato juice, 2 poached eggs on 2 slices of seven-grain toast (dry), 1/2 cup (~120 ml) low fat cottage cheese.
Lunch: Tuna salad with mayo on whole wheat bread, a mixed salad (lettuce, red peppers, carrots), extra virgin olive oil and vinegar.
Dinner: Broiled snapper, 1/2 cup brown rice, 1/2 cup three-bean salad, 1 cup cooked zucchini.

FATS

Dietary fats have been one of the missing nutritional links in endurance sports. In addition to supplying us with vast amounts of potential energy, fats help regulate our internal temperature, protect us from trauma, manage our hormones, and even help get calcium into our muscles and bones. Moreover, fats assist our important anti-inflammatory mechanism. They also make many foods taste good.

Fats Defined

The most common sources of fats are vegetable oils, butter, egg yolks, meats and cheeses.

Date/Day	Swim	Bike	Run			Notes
Mo						
Tu						
We						
Th						
Fr						
Sa						
Su						
Weekly Goal						
Weekly Actual						
Year To Date						

Make no mistake, these high-energy items can be harmful if overeaten. It is simply a question of balancing your intake of them; too much or too little is dangerous.

You also need to balance the *kinds* of fats you consume. To simplify matters, it helps to think in terms of A, B and C fats.

The A fats are unsaturated and are found in most vegetables, and in olive, safflower, peanut and corn oils. They are sometimes referred to by their chemical name, *omega-6*. Food concentrates of black currant seed, borage and primrose oil are also in this category.

The B fats are the saturated fats, found in dairy products, butter, meats and egg yolks; they contain the essential fat arachondonic acid. In recent years, B fats have been mistakenly viewed as "bad" fats, but scientific evidence has not really implicated them as destructive to health when consumed as part of a balanced diet.

C fats are another group of unsaturated fats, found in fish and beans, and in linseed, sesame, soy and walnut oils. They are chemically termed *omega-3*. This group also includes the food concentrates eicosapentanoic acid (EPA), found in flaxseed (linseed) and fish oil.

Most foods contain some combination of saturated and unsaturated fats. The unsaturated fats are of two types; polyunsaturated and the healthier monounsaturated. For example, extra-virgin olive oil contains mostly monounsaturated oil (77 percent), with about 9 percent polyunsaturated and 14 percent saturated.

The key in getting fats to work for you is balance; specifically, a balance of A, B and C fats in your diet. Equal amounts of each in the course of a week or month will help provide the balance you need. If you are a vegetarian and don't eat any B fats, then you need to take in equal amounts of A and C fats. Some of these will convert in your body to the B fats.

Burning Fat: The Key to Improved Endurance

Besides balancing your intake of fat, you must prevent the body from turning off the fat burning mechanism—this happens if you consume too much carbohydrate. Carbohydrates stimulate the release of the hormone insulin, which sends blood sugar to the cells and increases glycogen storage; essentially it compels your body to use more carbohydrates as fuel. But since glycogen storage space is small, insulin converts about 40 percent of your carbohydrates to fat for storage.

You can obtain 80 percent to 90 percent of your energy from fats. If you want to use more fats for energy (and thereby improve your endurance and performance), the insulin response must be moderated. Diets high in carbohydrates, especially refined carbohy-

Date/Day	Swim	Bike	Run			Notes
Mo						
Tu						
We						
Th						
Fr						
Sa						
Su						
Weekly Goal						
Weekly Actual						
Year To Date						

drates, result in more insulin being released and less fat being burned. Furthermore, if you don't provide your body with enough fat to use as energy, you may force it to use more sugar. This can lower the blood sugar and create "highs" and "lows," the mood swings people with blood sugar variations often feel. Mood swings are not the only reactions. Others include mental and/or physical fatigue, clumsiness, headaches, depression, allergies and other physical and mental impairments, depending on your susceptibility to an excess of sugar in the blood.

The team physician for the Motorola racing team, Dr. Massimo Testa of Italy, firmly believes that improved fat metabolism is the key to improving performance. "You need good fat burning for the aerobic engine," he says. He sees many athletes as being afraid of fats. "But the key to building a fat-burning system is to include the right fats in the diet. In Europe, we eat more fats in our diet than Americans do without the problems seen in America." He also believes that balancing fats is vital.

CARBOHYDRATES

It is fairly obvious that most, if not all, triathletes get a sufficient amount of carbohydrates in their diet. About the only potential concern is to make sure the carbohydrates you ingest are complex. The primary carbohydrate sources should include green leafy vegetables and starchy vegetables, grains, fruits and some dairy products. The food should be as fresh and "natural" as possible.

Are You Carbohydrate Intolerant?

We all evolved from the "caveman's diet," which consisted of meat and vegetables. Only recently has our physiology been asked to digest and metabolize larger amounts of sugar and starch, which is why many people may be unable to tolerate excess carbohydrate. Carbohydrate intolerance, which can be called *insulin resistance, hypoglycemia* or *hyperinsulinism,* often causes fatigue (both mental and physical) and low blood sugar, resulting in a craving for sweets or caffeine; intestinal bloating; sleepiness; increased fat storage and weight and sometimes depression. Long-term problems can include increased triglycerides and high blood pressure.

If you have these symptoms and also have been training with little or no loss of body fat and a decrease in your performance, you may be carbohydrate intolerant to some degree. To find out if you are, try a two-week diet that eliminates most breads, pastas, sweets, fruits and fruit juices, potatoes, milk and yogurt. Do this with the help of your doctor.

If you feel better at the end of the two weeks, you can suspect carbohydrate intolerance. Then, begin to add a few carbohydrates to your diet until you reach an amount that causes your symptoms to recur. This may be your optimal carbohydrate level. About 40 percent of the diet as carbohydrates will moderate the insulin response for most people;

Date/Day	Swim	Bike	Run			Notes
Mo						
Tu						
We						
Th						
Fr						
Sa						
Su						
Weekly Goal						
Weekly Actual						
Year To Date						

that leaves 30 percent for protein and 30 percent for fats.

If these ratios are successful with you, you will notice that

• You don't feel hungry between meals

• You don't experience fatigue or light-headedness

• Your physical and mental energy levels are higher

• Your metabolism is much more efficient

PROTEIN

The recommended daily allowance (RDA) for protein has been revised at least 10 times since 1943 and continues to be a topic for debate. Today, many experts in the field seem to feel that the current RDA value of 0.8 g/kg body weight is too low; some suggest amounts three to four times the RDA. People involved in activities that build muscle and endurance, or that subject their bodies to recurring trauma (as in running) may need a larger protein intake. Once optimal body size is attained and growth stabilizes, there is still significant and continuous turnover of tissue protein, especially in training athletes. In addition to muscle and other tissue growth and repair, protein is used for energy. The amount of energy contributed may be as high as 15 percent.

The traditional view that higher protein intakes are only required in weight lifters is outdated by studies showing that aerobic exercise may increase the need for protein more than anaerobic muscle-building exercise. This is because increased mitochondrial protein concentration of skeletal muscle occurs with endurance training. This process allows for more effective use of carbohydrate and fat since the mitochondria is the primary site of beta-oxidation, or fat burning. Therefore, increased protein intake can improve the work capacity of athletes.

Other studies also show that protein needs for those engaged in exercise are higher. Recent work concluding that actual protein needs are much higher than RDA recommendations is based on the use of radioactive tracers that identify the CO_2 (carbon dioxide) portion of the amino acid molecule. Moreover, researchers have expanded upon the traditional method of determining protein breakdown by examining the excretion of urea (which contains nitrogen from the protein).

Current research shows that as exercise increases, the concentration of plasma urea rises dramatically in sweat. Earlier studies, especially research on which RDA levels are based, only measured the nitrogen in urine, but failed to consider the amount of urea lost in sweat, clearly an important means of excreting the nitrogen from protein breakdown during exercise.

Date/Day	Swim	Bike	Run			Notes
Mo						
Tu						
We						
Th						
Fr						
Sa						
Su						
Weekly Goal						
Weekly Actual						
Year To Date						

Furthermore, urea production may not accurately reflect all aspects of protein break-down. The oxidation of plasma and intracellular leucine, an essential amino acid, increases significantly during moderate exercise, regardless of any change in urea produc-tion. Thus, those just beginning an exercise program have a substantially increased demand for protein, from both the muscle tissue and the metabolism.

VITAMINS AND MINERALS

Once your body gets the proper amounts of carbohydrate, protein and fat, using these macronutrients to create energy, promote growth and maintain health is the job of micronutrients—the vitamins and minerals. They promote the important chemical reac-tions that take place in the body every second. All known vitamins and minerals are sig-nificant for athletic function because they are necessary for health, some being more vital than others. The amounts required and specific needs for a particular vitamin or mineral vary from one person to another.

A unique aspect of some minerals is their ability to dissolve into electrically charged par-ticles called *electrolytes*. The most important electrolytes are sodium and potassium, which regulate the balance of nutrients, water and waste material in the cells. Electrolytes also preserve a proper electrical gradient so that muscles can contract properly.

In general, you should aim to ensure that your diet meets all your needs for vitamins and minerals. If additional needs develop, nutritional supplements can be considered. How-ever, there is no particular performance-enhancing vitamin or mineral.

The nutrition chapter was compiled and written by Dr. Phil Maffetone. He is an applied kinesiologist with a Bachelor of Science degree in human biology and a Doctorate in Chiropractic. He has treated and trained many national and world-class athletes, such as triathletes Mark Allen, Donna Peters and Mike Pigg, and runners Lorraine Moller and Priscilla Welch.

Heart Rate Monitor Training

Athletes: Ray Browning, USA; Pauli Kiuru, Finland; Henrik Nöb-belin, Sweden
Race: 1995 Säter Triathlon

Eight kilometers into the run, "the gang of three" are still over four
minutes behind the leader, Joachim Willén of Sweden

◀ ─────────────────────────

The heart rate monitor, as we know it, was developed in Finland. With their great tradition of endurance sports, the Finns proceeded to establish simple and practical procedures for optimizing the use of their creation. Their methods work—for Pauli Kiuru, Bennie Lindberg, Magnus Lönnqvist and Teemu Vesala. They will work for you.

The objective of this chapter is to combine some of the latest research—in itself open to interpretation—with the practical experience of the Finns, arguably the world's leading practitioners of triathlon training with heart rate monitors. If you are not familiar with the basic principles of exercise physiology, there is a list of definitions on page 24.

Warning: The field of exercise physiology is constantly evolving, which is one of the reasons experts disagree, sometimes strongly. For instance, the question of how to interpret the aerobic and anaerobic thresholds probably occasions more dissension among athletes and exercise physiologists of good will than any other training matter open to disagreement. However, most agree that if you train right, you will go faster and longer at a certain heart rate and it will seem more effortless to you.

The Heart Rate Monitor
Your heart rate monitor has three parts:

• A wrist monitor (looks like a digital watch)

• A sensor/transmitter (a flexible plastic stripe, often black)

• An elastic chest band

To use the monitor, attach the sensor/transmitter to your chest with the chest band, and strap the monitor to your wrist. If the monitor does not display your heart rate, put some saliva on the sensor/transmitter next to your skin to increase the conductivity. After you have reread the warnings on page 12, you're ready to roll.

Date/Day	Swim	Bike	Run			Notes
Mo						
Tu						
We						
Th						
Fr						
Sa						
Su						
Weekly Goal						
Weekly Actual						
Year To Date						

HOW TO USE A HEART RATE MONITOR

The heart rate monitor is an excellent tool for the serious athlete. The monitor gives a continuous read-out of what's really happening to your system, your heart in particular, when you expose it to stress. And your heart never lies.

Fixed Heart Rate Zones: A False Assumption

For competitive or recreational athletes, there are no universal fixed percentages of the MHR that will optimally improve performance. Yes, there *are* observable correlations between a person's MHR and what is happening physiologically in the body when one exercises—but they are not that obvious. First, the heart rate correlations are only approximations. Second, they are highly individual. And third, they are not static, but rather dynamic over time. To train with a goal of maintaining certain fixed percentages of your MHR, therefore, carries with it a high risk of undertraining, or worse (triathletes can be quite driven), overtraining.

Cardiovascular Training Objectives

Many exercise physiologists believe that raising your AT is the most important factor in enhancing your performance in a distance race; others tend to focus on the aerobic threshold. In his book *Swimming Even Faster,* Ernest Maglischo writes: "The purpose of endurance training is to improve aerobic capacity, allowing athletes to swim faster with less reliance on anaerobic metabolism so that lactic acid will accumulate at a slower speed." Actually, improvement in your thresholds reflects a series of physiological changes in your body such as a VO_2max increase, a reduction in muscle lactate production and an improvement in lactate removal from your muscles. Continuous training also increases your heart's stroke volume, your blood volume and the number of red blood cells.

Testing with a Heart Rate Monitor with Access to a Laboratory

In order to get maximum benefit from the heart rate monitor, the Finnish athletes undergo testing in a lab—on a treadmill or an ergometer bicycle—while their blood lactate levels are measured. Then tests are done on a track. Sometimes lab testing is not possible, in which case only the track is used. *All training is based on the most recent results.*

The Direct Test. The lab test on a treadmill is called a *direct test,* which means that the load is increased gradually (often every three minutes) until exhaustion. Blood lactate levels are continuously measured. Let's say you reach your aerobic capacity at a pace of 4 min/km with a heart rate of 145 BPM, and that your MHR is 185. Your aerobic capacity is thus 40 BPM below your MHR at a pace of 4 min/km. (Generally, the Finns have found that the aerobic capacity is approximately 40 (+/-5) BPM and the anaerobic capacity approximately 20 (+/-10) BPM below the MHR. For a less fit person, these heart rates may vary more. It is also normal to have different values for running and cycling.)

The Track Test. In the track test you determine your aerobic capacity without measuring

Date/Day	Swim	Bike	Run			Notes
Mo						
Tu						
We						
Th						
Fr						
Sa						
Su						
Weekly Goal						
Weekly Actual						
Year To Date						

lactates. Let's say that with a heart rate of 145 BPM you now require 4:10 to run one kilometer. The difference is 10 seconds. This means that under real conditions you can expect your aerobic pace to be 10 seconds slower. If your pace is 10 seconds *faster* on the track, you are probably unaccustomed to running on a treadmill. As you get used to the treadmill, your track and treadmill results will converge.

The Swim Test. If you have access to lab equipment at your pool, you can do the following test: swim 10 by 200 m with 30 seconds rest. Start slow and go progressively faster for each 200 m swim. The last 200 m is at max speed. You measure time, heart rate, lactates and strokes per lap. These data will also show how efficiently you swim.

Testing without Access to a Laboratory
If you do not have access to a lab, you can do the following tests on a track.

The Max Test. Warm up for about 15 minutes. Then run 100 m fast two to three times. Then run 400 m by accelerating so that for the last 60 to 80 m you are going as fast as you can (you must exhaust yourself). Check your maximum heart rate. Your aerobic and anaerobic capacities are approximately 40 and 20 BPM below your MHR, respectively.

The Aerobic Test. After warm-up, run the same kilometer as described earlier at your aerobic capacity (say 145 BPM). Early in the season your time may be 4:10. Later in the season, you should be able to run the same kilometer faster with the same heart rate. You may also factor in your perceived level of effort to determine your aerobic level. Think of this intensity as: "Fast, but I can keep going forever, or almost forever." Alternative aerobic tests are: a two mile run, or Mark Allen's five-mile track test on page 88.

Heart Rate Based Training
Optimal training is based on a given work load; in our example an aerobic threshold of 145 BPM. For the next few months, an LSD run—by definition, almost completely aerobic—would be between 120 and 130 BPM, and an AT run would be in the 145 to 160 BPM range. During high-intensity intervals, the heart rate would go above 160 BPM.

Important: As you get fitter, and if you train properly, your thresholds will move upward. What may have been an anaerobic session early in the season will become a primarily aerobic session later on and years later may be an endurance pace that you can keep up "indefinitely." Again, it's helpful to check how the elite athletes modify their training to account for such seasonal and annual improvements.

Your Morning Resting Heart Rate
You also need to measure and record your RHR before you get out of bed every morning. As you get fitter, your RHR drops. An elevation of five or more beats per minute from your present norm is a sign that your system is overstressed. The source could be impend-

Date/Day	Swim	Bike	Run			Notes
Mo						
Tu						
We						
Th						
Fr						
Sa						
Su						
Weekly Goal						
Weekly Actual						
Year To Date						

ing illness (cold, flu, etc.), overtraining, anxiety or lack of sleep. Or you may not have yet recovered from previous workouts (in which case you need to rest some).

The Orthostatic Heart Rate

A unique method for monitoring yourself is the "orthostatic heart rate method," developed by Dr. Heikki Tikkanen from Finland. It is particularly useful to determine training recovery and your adaptation to changes in altitude, climate, time zones and so on. The theory behind the test is that the stress your body is exposed to when you go from a lying to a standing position is considerable, and that the way your body manages this stress can be used as an indicator of how well recovered you are.

Upon waking in the morning, get up, walk around and follow your normal morning routines for 15 minutes. Don't eat or drink anything, except water. Then go back to bed and rest for 10 minutes. Then get up and stand still for six minutes while monitoring your heart rate. Do not move. Your heart rate curve will look similar to the figure below. Notice that as you stand up, your heart rate will spike and then gradually decline toward your resting heart rate.

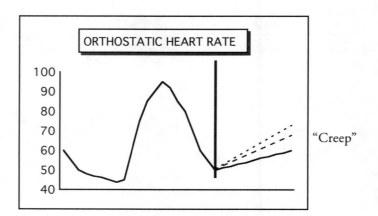

After a few minutes of standing, your heart rate will again start to creep up. This increase (pictured to the right of the vertical bar) is important. If it's less than 10 BPM, you are well recovered. Go race! And 10 to 15 BPM is still OK. More than 25 BPM is bad—your system is trying to cope with some extraordinary stress. You need further rest.

HEART RATE MONITOR USAGE AMONG HAWAII IRONMAN FINISHERS

Most top triathletes use a heart rate monitor for training and racing. In the 1994 and 1995 Hawaii Ironman races, for example, some competitors made good use of the monitor. A representative sample is listed below.

Date/Day	Swim	Bike	Run			Notes
Mo						
Tu						
We						
Th						
Fr						
Sa						
Su						
Weekly Goal						
Weekly Actual						
Year To Date						

Dr. Gayle Bilsland

A 45-year-old triathlete from Scottsdale, Arizona, Gayle Bilsland is one of the top age-group triathletes in the United States and has finished twelve Ironman races. She placed second in her age-group in Hawaii in both 1994 and 1995. Originally a cyclist, Gayle doesn't feel that she needs any of the bells and whistles of the more advanced monitors: "It's just a reality check for me out there. All I want is an instantaneous read-out." She doesn't keep track of her AT, but has measured her maximum heart rate at 180 BPM.

Training. Preparing for the Hawaii Ironman, her favorite long distance rides are at 140 to 150 BPM for several hours. Otherwise, her favorite bike workouts are 1-2-3-4-3-2-1 pyramids. She goes hard, maintaining 170 BPM, for one minute, then spins for one to two minutes (to get her heart rate down to 135), then rides hard for two minutes, and so on. Her run intervals are very similar: "I guess I'm not very scientific about it, but these pyramids are really interchangeable. But in both cycling and running it takes several minutes to get my heart rate down near the end."

Racing. After she started using her monitor regularly she has noticed a significant increase in her race performances: "It really made a difference, I noticed huge improvements." In the 1994 race, she had a plan to let the monitor guide her to a steady effort throughout bike ride, but destiny dictated otherwise: "I wanted it to keep myself from getting lulled into going too easy and to avoid charging after somebody else." Unfortunately, her monitor didn't pick up her signals on the bike, and on the run she doesn't like to use it, anyway: "By the time I get to the run, I just go as fast as I can."

Ray Browning

Ray Browning from Colorado is a world class multisport athlete and a seven-time Ironman winner around the globe. Ray has been using a monitor for several years and prefers the Polar Favor and the Vantage XL. He uses them for both training and racing.

Training. Ray uses the monitor to establish his thresholds every six to eight weeks. The workouts are based on the most current values. He likes to do three key workouts every week: a two- to four-hour over-distance (OD) session, a one-hour interval session just below his AT and a lactate threshold session.

His OD session is at 130 to 142 BPM, which is well below his AT: "The monitor forces me to run really slow during the uphills and faster during the downhills to maintain my heart rate range."

One of his favorite interval sessions is on the bike. He'll keep his working heart rate at about 170 BPM for a few minutes with a recovery rate of 130 BPM. The length of the efforts and recoveries depends on the shape he's in. These sessions generally take about

Date/Day	Swim	Bike	Run			Notes
Mo						
Tu						
We						
Th						
Fr						
Sa						
Su						
Weekly Goal						
Weekly Actual						
Year To Date						

one hour, including warm-up and warm-down. The lactate threshold sessions are performed on a track. They often consist of three to eight 4-minute cycles of stress-rest with less rest than in the above interval sessions. He'll do 1,000 m repeats and not allow his heart rate to recover more than 20 or 30 BPM.

Racing. In long-distance races, Ray likes to wear the monitor during the swim. During the bike ride, he's very careful to ride below his AT during the first 40 to 50 km. He also points out that in higher temperatures, the heart rate will drift upward because of the body's need to cool itself: "I'd say a drift of about five beats per minute is acceptable."

He also provides some valuable input on how to evaluate other "drifts" during long races: "If you have a problem keeping your heart rate up, it is most often nutritionally related, and keeping it down is dehydration." In other words, if your heart rate is below your selected range and you have a hard time getting it up—assuming, of course, that your "range" is properly selected—then you need to eat. Conversely, if it shoots through the roof and your pace is dismal, you need to drink. If it were October, and you found yourself left on Queen Kaahumanu highway, you'd give your right arm for this kind of advice!

After about the 16- to 18-mile mark on the run it's a different story, however: "At this point it's a struggle. I tell myself that 'OK, this tool has been as useful as it needed to be. Now I must focus on bringing it home.' You need to dig deep and, heart rate or no heart rate, that is a mental issue."

It is clear that Ray takes a scientific approach to training and racing. But he adds a healthy dose of common sense and humor to the equation: "The ultimate goal of training is to get my heart rate work threshold as close to my maximum heart rate as possible. But, my ultimate racing plan always has to include a plan B: what if my monitor doesn't work? If there is a power line along the race course, I can kiss my monitor good-bye."

Lesley Cens-McDowell

Former runner, Lesley Cens-McDowell from West Chester, Pennsylvania is a six-time age-group winner in Hawaii. She has entered the race nine times. Her 45 to 49 age-group win in 1995—at the age of 49—was her third straight! The other athletes in her age-group are, no doubt, happy that she's finally turning 50.

She has used a Polar Accurex II for about two years. Her maximum heart rate is 179 and her AT about 155 to 160 BPM. She has something of a love-hate relationship with her monitor: "Sometimes I don't use it because I want to go out and run how I feel. I have an efficient speed and the monitor forces me to run too slow and do things I don't want to do. But it's really helpful on the bike."

Date/Day	Swim	Bike	Run			Notes
Mo						
Tu						
We						
Th						
Fr						
Sa						
Su						
Weekly Goal						
Weekly Actual						
Year To Date						

Training. She has three key workouts per week, one long distance, one interval and one AT. The long distance session is normally a five-hour bike ride at about 70 to 80 percent of her max: "Actually, 80 percent is a bit high." Her interval sessions consist of three to ten minutes at 80 to 90 percent of maximum, followed by a recovery period in which she lets her heart rate go down to 125 BPM. She does six to eight of these intervals. Her AT session is about one hour of riding with an average heart rate of around 155: "I do these workouts with 50 or 60 guys. We go around a two-mile loop and I just sit in the pack."

Racing. For short-course racing she has traditionally not used her monitor: "It's pedal to the metal. You get a time, you have a heart rate and you cross a finish line."

However, she made some interesting modifications for the 1995 season. First, she took the year off from racing, in the traditional sense. She entered five races, all as part of her training and with the only goal that of staying at her AT: "When I did race, my goal was not to focus on who was ahead of me, but to concentrate on and stay at my AT. It was just me and my monitor and no pre-race stress. It was fun. My average heart rate at the end would usually be 155." Oh, and by the way, she would usually win.

On Ironman race day, she finds the monitor very useful. On the bike and run, she sets her target range at 132 to 146 BPM: "In 1994, I had a hard time keeping that rate up on the bike, and I don't know why."

In 1995, the plan was the same, but because of bad wind conditions, she found herself braking a lot for fear of getting blown off the bike. Consequently, her heart rate would repeatedly drop out of range: "During this bike leg was the first time I wished I weighed 50 pounds more! I learned later how I should have ridden through it. Oh, well."

On the run, she is always very steady: "My average on the run in 1994 was 138, with 19 minutes and 10 seconds above my target rate and 4 minutes below. I felt like a robot out there." She essentially repeated her performance in 1995, but this year she was in the peculiar situation of being 34 minutes down after the bike: "The robot returned. I forgot about the monitor and just ran what felt like a strong and steady pace. I think the only reason I wear the monitor on the run is not for the heart rate numbers, but so I can occasionally check on pace per mile and make sure I'm not going too fast or doing something stupid." She did nothing stupid—and ended up winning her age-group by 23 minutes.

Teemu Vesala

Teemu Vesala from Finland won the Ironman Canada in 1994. More importantly—the Finnish nation takes cross country skiing very seriously—he is a seven-time cross country skiing champion. He uses the Polar brand, with the Accurex II being his favorite. On the bike he has a Polar Edge: "All I need is the heart rate display to see where I am." In races

Date/Day	Swim	Bike	Run			Notes
Mo						
Tu						
We						
Th						
Fr						
Sa						
Su						
Weekly Goal						
Weekly Actual						
Year To Date						

he uses the Sport Tester so he can download the results to a computer after the race.

Teemu finds that his bike rates are five to ten BPM under his run rates, across the board. For instance, his AT on the run often measures about 180, and on the bike 170 to 175.

Training. Having the benefit of more scientific support than most athletes, Teemu has a very clear picture of how to use the monitor, but he claims that the most useful application is a very simple one: "I use the average heart rate to estimate how hard the training was. And I estimate the improvement in my conditioning by using the average heart rate and average speed over courses that I know." The only variable becomes the weather conditions. And with practice, anyone can assess this variable pretty accurately.

When he lived far from a pool in Finland, he used the monitor in a very creative way: with a wetsuit in a cold water lake. (Even with a wetsuit, these swims are possible only during the months of June, July and August.) He programed the monitor to beep at upper limit and recovery heart rates. Voilá. Without the trappings of a pool, tiled walls and lane lines, you have "chlorine free and organic repeats."

Racing. In long races, Teemu rides with a heart rate in the 150 to 160 BPM range: "Except for early in the bike, I would not go over 160 very long. If you push hard early on the bike, it'll cost you later in the run." Later in the ride, he finds that fatigue makes it difficult to keep his heart rate up: "I then use the monitor to make sure I stay above 150." On the run, it's the same story: "If you start out running with a very high heart rate, it's difficult to get it down. You must start out relaxed and easy." But if the race is going well, he doesn't worry too much about his heart rate, particularly in the latter portion of the run: "If it's 180 and I feel OK, I just go."

Summary
On race day, Ironman triathletes seem to benefit the most from the monitors in the general area of pacing: stay below the target rate early in the race and try to maintain it toward the end.

Training Secrets from the Elite

Athlete: Mark Allen, USA
Race: 1995 Hawaii Ironman

About 4:30 behind Thomas "Hell on Wheels" Hellriegel from Germany, Mark turns down towards the Natural Energy Labs

← ─────────────────────────

This almanac features in-depth training information from five of the best triathletes in the world, as outlined in Table 3.

Athlete	Specialty	Topic
Mark Allen	Triathlon any distance	Training and peaking
Jeff Devlin	Duathlon/triathlon	AT-based training
Pauli Kiuru	Triathlon long distance	HRM-based training
Paula Newby-Fraser	Triathlon long distance	Training and peaking
Karen Smyers	Triathlon any distance	Training and racing

Table 3: Featured top athletes

MARK ALLEN

Voted Triathlete of the Decade, Mark is clearly the number one male multisport athlete in the world, and one of the best endurance athletes the world has ever seen. He wins duathlons and triathlons of any distance and at any elevation, regardless of climate and race course topography. Mark has successfully battled the Kona sun and wind, the Swiss Alps, the French Riviera and Säter, Sweden. Each time he is the favorite going in and each time he wins.

The Three Phases of the Year

Mark divides his training and racing year into three phases. The first is two to three months long and consists of purely aerobic work, as well as weight training to increase strength. The second includes a preparation for the regular season with the addition of speed work, and also incorporates most of the regular season with both long and short races, as well as recovery periods. The third is the big push for the Hawaii Ironman.

Date/Day	Swim	Bike	Run			Notes
Mo						
Tu						
We						
Th						
Fr						
Sa						
Su						
Weekly Goal						
Weekly Actual						
Year To Date						

Patience. Mark generally starts his base work in January. He calls this his patience phase: "About once a week I push the top end of the aerobic range without going anaerobic. For instance, I would never do 'The Tuesday Run' [a fast anaerobic run in San Diego] during this phase; it's too fast." Though he feels you can only build your base up to a point, this is where the groundwork is laid: "I look at the base phase as building my engine. The longer I build my base, the larger the engine, but you can only build your engine so much in one year." A very long-term approach to training, indeed.

	Swim	Bike	Run	Other/Notes
Mo	4,000 m	30 miles	1 hour	Aerobic
Tu	4,000 m	—	1:15 hours	Aerobic
We	—	110 miles	30 min	Aerobic
Th	5,000 m	25 miles	—	Aerobic
Fr	—	60 miles	30 min	Aerobic
Sa	6,000 m	90 miles	50 min	Aerobic
Su	2,000 m	—	2 hours	Aerobic

Table 4: Training during Mark's patience phase

Well into the patience phase, he is able to go faster while maintaining the same aerobic heart rate range. A recent favorite has been to work on his leg turnover while maintaining a relatively low heart rate: "You need to find an ideally several-mile-long downgrade and just run at an even pace, concentrating on your leg turnover."

Every three weeks or so, he does a five-mile run to check progress. This aerobic run, sometimes conducted on a track, is always at the upper end of his aerobic range, or what he calls his "aerobic pace." For Mark this is approximately 150 BPM. "Early on, my aerobic pace will be at six minutes per mile. Three weeks later, I might be running a 5:40 pace with the same heart rate." In other words, the fitter you get, the faster your aerobic pace.[1] As the weeks go by and the long miles pile up, even Mark's patience wears thin—these sessions break the monotony and give him tangible proof that he's improving.

"In order to do these runs right, you need to determine the high end of your aerobic range," says Mark. He likes a formula used in his health club, Personalized Workout of La

---

[1.] Many years ago, Mark's aerobic pace at the end of his base training for the five-mile run was 6:35 minutes per mile. In 1993 it was 5:27 and in 1995 it was 5:20.

Date/Day	Swim	Bike	Run			Notes
Mo						
Tu						
We						
Th						
Fr						
Sa						
Su						
Weekly Goal						
Weekly Actual						
Year To Date						

Jolla. This formula was originally developed by Phil Maffetone: 180 minus your age plus/minus a correction factor. Table 5 shows how the formula would work for four different 35-year-olds, and for Mark himself:

Individual	Factor	Formula
"Couch potato"	-10	180 - 35 -10 = 135
"Weekend warrior"	-5	180 - 35 - 5 = 140
On a regular training program for years	0	180 - 35 = 145
Very fit person	+5	180 - 35 + 5 = 150
Mark Allen	+5	180 - 38 + 5 = 147

Table 5: Finding your upper aerobic range

During the patience phase, Mark is specifically training his enzyme system's ability to burn fat: "If you're attuned to your body, you get a very good feeling for when your body is burning fat."

Speedwork. About five to six weeks before his first race of the season, Mark adds some interval and anaerobic speed workouts while lowering his overall distance. At the same time, he will likely toss out the weight training from his schedule, which is for him a welcome relief: "I do weights out of necessity, not out of passion." The speedwork training phase lasts five to six weeks; he then tries to maintain that fitness level while racing, until sometime in July. Table 6 outlines a typical week during Mark's speedwork phase.

	Swim	Bike	Run	Notes/Other
Mo	3,000 m	40 miles	40 min	Easy
Tu	4,500 m	40 miles	1.5 hours on trails	Fartlek intervals
We		90 miles on hills	1 hour	Anaerobic bike
Th	3,000 m	Recovery ride	30 min	
Fr	3,000 m		AM: 50 min PM: 30 min	The only double-run day
Sa	5,000 m	90 miles	15 - 20 min	Transition run following the ride
Su		20 miles easy	Up to 2.5 hours	All aerobic

Table 6: Training during Mark's speedwork phase

Date/Day	Swim	Bike	Run			Notes
Mo						
Tu						
We						
Th						
Fr						
Sa						
Su						
Weekly Goal						
Weekly Actual						
Year To Date						

Mark has noticed that as he gets older, it becomes more difficult to maintain a longer period with a lot of anaerobic work: "A young person can do 10 to 12 weeks, while a 40-year-old only five and a 50-year-old none at all. I can do maybe six now. The key is to watch for a slowing of your pace at your maximum aerobic heart rate. When this happens, it's time to go back to your base-building phase."

At the end of his speedwork phase, Mark finds that he has reached a plateau. The plateau is an important signal. He knows that it's time to either slack off on the speedwork and rest more or go back to a few weeks of purely low-intensity aerobic training: "It's very subtle, but if your heart rate starts going up for a given effort in workouts, you know that you're on the edge—just resting won't help, you have to modify your training." He also monitors his resting heart rate for signs of overtraining.

Important: It is my opinion that the sensitivity, intelligence and confidence that Mark shows here is the most widely reproducible key to Mark's excellence over the years. He is sensitive enough to read his body's signals, intelligent enough to understand what they mean and confident enough to do something in response to them. This "doing something" may be training less, training differently or just resting.

Many other athletes would probably train through the plateau in an attempt to reach that illusive higher level of fitness. This strategy will fail. The likely result is, instead, mental burn-out, physical over-training, injury and a sub-par performance on race day. In Mark's own words: "Above all, if you're burned out, put a big 'R' for rest in your almanac, close it and put it away." Go play!

So, at the end of his speedwork phase, Mark cuts out the anaerobic workouts, decreases his training load and goes back to several weeks of aerobic recovery pace training. Since this occurs in the middle of the racing season, Mark has to balance the demands of racing well with those of staying fit, healthy and uninjured. He takes a couple of weeks without racing and designates them as aerobic and fun: "In just a few weeks I can rebuild my aerobic base." In fact, in the last several years, he has completely stopped training for one week in early August, which, as the world has seen, has resulted in great late season success: "Yes, I take the week off."

Toward the end of this phase, it's time to prepare for the year-end races, generally culminating for Mark in Hawaii. He says, "If you are going to peak for a two-hour race, throw in some weights and high-intensity shorter workouts—if you're doing The Ironman, get the miles in."

The Push. Eight weeks before The Hawaii Ironman in October, Mark starts preparing for the final leg of his annual triathlon journey. The Push consists of four hard weeks and

Date/Day	Swim	Bike	Run			Notes
Mo						
Tu						
We						
Th						
Fr						
Sa						
Su						
Weekly Goal						
Weekly Actual						
Year To Date						

four taper weeks—he used to do five hard and three taper weeks. "I never race during these eight weeks," Mark adds.

The first four weeks are all-encompassing and require a level of dedication and effort beyond most normal human experiences: "You've got to sit down with your loved ones and explain to them what's in store. Sleep is paramount, everything else goes." Week by week, he gradually builds his mileage and intensity until, by week four, he's riding 500

	Swim	Bike	Run	Notes/Other
Mo	4,000 m	80 miles	30 min	Easy
Tu	—	120 - 150 miles	50 min	Long ride, last 1/3 anaerobic
We	5,000 m	—	AM: 1.5 hours PM: 30 min easy	Hilly and hard, sometimes extremely anaerobic
Th	4,000 m	75 miles	40 min	Flat (no hills)
Fr	4,000 m	110 miles	50 min	Hilly bike and run
Sa	5,000 m	Speed	Trails (or track)	Everything is short and fast
Su	6,000 m	30 miles easy	2.5 hours	Aerobic

Table 7: Training during Mark's "Push"

miles and running 80 miles per week. The trick is to combine speed and endurance, which is best accomplished by doing very long intervals—up to 20 minutes each—or by incorporating some anaerobic periods into the long workouts. For instance, toward the end of a five- to six-hour ride, he'll do some anaerobic work: "If this was base work, I would just finish the ride. But now, after you've been riding for several hours, surge for 10 minutes, then recover and do this a few more times."

In Boulder, there's a 15-mile run that Mark considers "extremely anaerobic." The first 10 km are uphill and hard, followed by a 5 km section of downhill cruising and finally a 10 km section of rolling hills: "The last six miles I consider 'recover at a high heart rate'—which means you don't. I would never do this run during the base work period." A somewhat similar type of workout might be 16 km with a four to six km surge, or a long gradual hill, towards the end.

Ideally, Mark believes, you should try to do weights twice weekly, though he finds it hard: "You're pretty beat up from all this; you have to decide. I normally let it go."

Date/Day	Swim	Bike	Run			Notes
Mo						
Tu						
We						
Th						
Fr						
Sa						
Su						
Weekly Goal						
Weekly Actual						
Year To Date						

The Taper

A few years ago, he increased his tapering from three to four weeks: "You need four weeks to build yourself back up 100 percent after the hard training." The chart below shows how Mark tapers over the last five weeks before the most important race of the year.

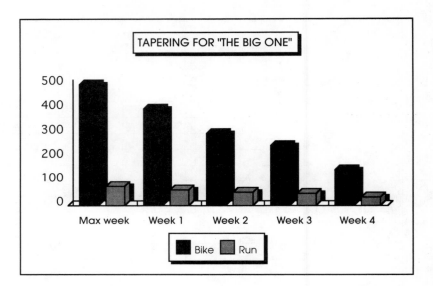

His cycling decreases from a maximum of 500 miles during the fourth hard week, to 400 miles during the first taper week and 150 miles the last week of the taper. The corresponding numbers for running are 80 to 65 to 35 miles: "The mileage for the fourth week of tapering *includes* the race day mileage. For me, the Ironman." Read Mark's quote again! It ranks as one of the most important sentences of this almanac. Because, as you know by now, *performance = stress + rest.*

Also, Mark feels that nutritional requirements during the last eight weeks are above normal and advises you to pay particular attention to what you eat. Eat as if your life depended on it: "Vitamin supplements are important, and you have an increased need for protein. Normally, I eat red meat, say, every one to two months; now I'll eat it every three to four days. If your body craves it, eat it. Just don't become a junk food junkie."

More Training Tips from Mark

- Except during the patience phase, always do two long-distance and two speed workouts per week, one each cycling and running. These are your *key workouts.* You build everything else around them.

Date/Day	Swim	Bike	Run			Notes
Mo						
Tu						
We						
Th						
Fr						
Sa						
Su						
Weekly Goal						
Weekly Actual						
Year To Date						

- During the speedwork phase, designate no more than two anaerobic days a week: "One per week might be all you can handle, which is fine. You've got to recover."

- Train your weak areas. For instance, find out whether you are better at climbing or at "powering the flats" on the bike. If you're a good climber, you need to power the flats.

- Do your long runs and speedwork on soft-surfaced trails: "Trails are much more real-world. The track is just too unrealistic with what you'll be facing on race day."

- About eight days before a race, in order to boost your body's oxygen-extracting capacity, go just above your AT and hold it for 15 minutes: "You do this and your oxygen-extracting capacity goes way up."

- Use a heart rate monitor: "I always use the most basic one."

- Stretch (Mark does static active stretching).

JEFF DEVLIN

Jeff Devlin continues to excel at all distances of both duathlons and triathlons. He has won many of the world's most prestigious duathlons. As a triathlete, he excels at pretty much any distance. This success is due to his unique talent, of course, but also to the way he trains. Over the last few years, however, he has modified his training: "I seem to train less and less every year and get more out of what I do. The schedule [Table 8] stays the same throughout the year, with some modifications when I am racing and/or getting ready for the Ironman or the Powerman."

	Swim	Bike	Run
Mo	4 - 6,000 yards	1 - 2 hours easy or 1 - 2 hours aerobic threshold intervals	45 - 60 min easy or 60 - 90 min track/hill workout
Tu	4 - 6,000 yards	3 hours AT intervals or "Tuesday Night Ride"	45 - 60 min aerobic
We	4 - 6,000 yards	OFF or easy MTB	1.5 - 2.5 hours
Th	4 - 6,000 yards	3 - 6 hours "distance"	
Fr	4 - 6,000 yards		45 - 60 min aerobic
Sa		3 - 4 hours tempo threshold intervals or continuous tempo	<1.5 hours tempo threshold intervals or continuous tempo
Su	~2,000 m easy		

Table 8: Jeff Devlin's training

He now swims in the distance lane with a university swim team, each workout typically

Date/Day	Swim	Bike	Run			Notes
Mo						
Tu						
We						
Th						
Fr						
Sa						
Su						
Weekly Goal						
Weekly Actual						
Year To Date						

5,000 yards. He rides four times a week and he runs five days a week: "I don't do any double runs anymore and I never do a track workout after a race weekend. My track workouts are usually straightforward 800s or mile repeats with varying intensity [AT or above] with either complete or incomplete rest. I also do weights two to three times per week, usually on the hard run days."

AT-Based Training

Jeff believes in the heart rate monitor and AT-based training (as opposed to aerobic threshold or maximum-heart-rate-based training). Consequently, most if not all workouts are monitored by how his heart is responding to a given load and how that load relates to his *current AT.* He monitors his AT with lab tests, as well as his own training tests: "All intensities are based on my most current tests. I train my AT best at 10 to 15 BPM below the actual threshold." Table 9 outlines his intensity levels.

Workout Type	Percent of AT
Short intervals	95 - 100
Intervals/tempo	90 - 95
Aerobic threshold	85 - 90
Endurance/distance	75 - 85
Easy	65 - 75

Table 9: Jeff Devlin's Intensity Key

Tapering and Peaking

Jeff likes to count back six to eight weeks from *The Race:* "Ideally, you want to be training consistently leading up to this period. You also want to be fresh before you start this cycle so a low-volume, easy week beforehand is a good idea." Then build up your training for three to five weeks. Three weeks before the big race, decrease by 20 to 25 percent the volume while maintaining the intensity. Two weeks before, take two to four days to recover from the past weeks' training, then get back into your normal schedule until four days before the race. The last four days are easy: "Rest and stay loose by stretching, massage and doing only easy, short workouts. On race day, go fast!"

PAULI KIURU

"We have no secrets." These are the words of Seppo Nuuttila, coach of Pauli Kiuru and several other top European triathletes, Peter Kropko and Bernhard Oliver to mention a couple. "Only that somewhere you have really good athletes; it doesn't matter what country, and you must find them."

Date/Day	Swim	Bike	Run			Notes
Mo						
Tu						
We						
Th						
Fr						
Sa						
Su						
Weekly Goal						
Weekly Actual						
Year To Date						

Or, as is the case with Seppo, they must find him. Pauli did, back in 1985. One day he called the coach up and said essentially, "Seppo, I want to be one of the two or three best triathletes in the world. Do you want to coach me?" Thus began an athlete/coach relationship that has lasted for a decade and resulted in 24 Ironman races, with seven victories. He has several top-three finishes in Kona. In 1993, Pauli was in the lead until the 16-mile mark, where Mark Allen caught him. Pauli ended up second, a full six minutes ahead of third place. Pauli is one of only three triathletes to break 8:15 in Kona.

A Long-Term Plan

"For great success, you need to work with somebody for many years; two or three is not long enough." The key is to set up a long-term goal, several years into the future and then plan backwards through the years, and the months of the first year. In Pauli's case, they figured it would take five or six years to reach his goal, so they first established a three-year plan.

Then they tested Pauli's physiological work capacity and skills in the three triathlon disciplines—in fact about 15 different aspects of skill and physiological capacity were tested. Next, they set up a one-year plan, with an attainable training volume target that Pauli could reach in six months. After the six months of aerobic build-up training came three months of pre-competition training and finally three months of racing.

The structure of this training plan has remained the same through the years. In fact, it has been used by other endurance athletes in the Nordic countries, particularly in the winter sports, with great success. Each month is broken into three weeks of training and one week of recovery: performance = stress + rest. Says Seppo, "It takes the body three weeks to adapt to a certain training level, and then you need to rest." The one-week recovery periods are designed to let the body recover from the previous three weeks and prepare for the next three weeks.

The unit of measurement is time, not distance. The first year, Pauli started with 13-hour weeks and had increased to 18-hour weeks by the end of the base building period. If you cannot attain and keep a certain training level, you have to decrease the number of hours. In Pauli's case, he gets migraine headaches if the training load is too heavy. "We then go down about three hours per week to allow him to adapt," says Seppo.

In later years, Pauli started his aerobic base training at 18 hours, and recently as high as 20 or 21 hours. The maximum number of hours he would ever train is 25 to 28 hours. This is an extreme amount of training, requiring a lot of quality rest and pretty much nothing else in your life. During the entire six-month aerobic period, 80 to 90 percent of the training—again, as measured by time trained—would be aerobic work, and 10 to 20 percent anaerobic.

Date/Day	Swim	Bike	Run			Notes
Mo						
Tu						
We						
Th						
Fr						
Sa						
Su						
Weekly Goal						
Weekly Actual						
Year To Date						

In recent years and toward the end of the pre-competitive season, Pauli would change his schedule to two weeks of hard training and one week of recovery. There are two reasons for this: first, the intensity is so high that three consecutive weeks of hard training would start to tear down, not build up, and second, Pauli is getting older and needs more rest.

Periodic Testing

After each month of training, Pauli goes through a series of tests: "These are not laboratory tests, just test training to get a feeling for the progress we are making," says Seppo. The test parameters are always the same: heart rate, lactate levels and speed. "These data taken together will give you the progress information you need. To me it's particularly satisfying to see that the Germans are now using this."

Table 10 shows how Pauli's training values have improved over the years for a one-kilometer timed run.

Threshold	Year	Heart Rate (BPM)	Time (min)	Blood Lactate (mM)
Aerobic	1985	147	4:37	0.9
Aerobic	1990	143	4:05	1.0
Aerobic	1995	145	3:50	1.2
Anaerobic	1985	167	3:48	2.3
Anaerobic	1990	162	3:35	2.4
Anaerobic	1995	163	3:20	2.7

Table 10: Pauli Kiuru's threshold values

Lab Tests

Three times a year—at the beginning of base training, at the end of base training and right before the final push for the most important race of the season—Pauli goes through more comprehensive laboratory tests. These test results give a complete picture of Pauli's conditioning.

For instance, Pauli's MHR is 186 to 189 BPM. His AT on the bike is 151 to 153, and on the run 160 to 163. His aerobic threshold on the bike is 135 to 137, and on the run 141 to 145. His best VO_2max values are 82 ml/kg for cycling and 74 ml/kg for running.

Regarding specific blood lactate concentrations, the Finns are well aware of the generally recognized 4 mM level for the AT. But since Pauli is an ultra-distance specialist, Seppo

Date/Day	Swim	Bike	Run			Notes
Mo						
Tu						
We						
Th						
Fr						
Sa						
Su						
Weekly Goal						
Weekly Actual						
Year To Date						

likes to use a 2 mM level for most of Pauli's AT work, though they do go higher.

Strength and Circuit Training

Pauli does strength training—a combination of free weights and machines—twice weekly during the base training and pre-competitive periods, and once weekly during the competitive season.

In addition to these strengthening exercises in the gym, Seppo's athletes also go through a circuit training program, using no weights or resistance machinery. These exercises are primarily aimed at the trunk, arms and legs, and include sit-ups, crunches, jumping, and so on. Seppo believes that a strong trunk (abdominals, obliques and back muscles) is critical for athletic success.

Tapering and Peaking

Like most athletes, Pauli uses two kinds of tapering and peaking schemes. The first, which he calls "inside of training," is designed as an in-season preparation for an important race. Table 11 shows how Pauli prepares for the half-Ironman Säter Triathlon in Sweden, which is always scheduled the last Sunday of June or the first Sunday of July. For this race, Pauli starts to taper one week before the race.

	Swim	Bike	Run	Other
Mo		PM: 2 hours easy	AM: 1 hour fartlek	
Tu		2 hours fartlek (100 to 160 BPM), incl. 2 x 5 km at 95% of max		
We	AM: 1 hour swim technique, 5 x 200 m fast			PM: strength training with free weights
Th			45 min run	Pace depending on how he feels
Fr	30 min easy	30 min easy		
Sa		30 min easy	15 min easy	

Table 11: Peaking for the Säter Triathlon

The second scheme is longer and designed for the most important race of the season; for Pauli, traditionally the Ironman in Hawaii. Table 12 shows how Pauli has prepared for

Date/Day	Swim	Bike	Run			Notes
Mo						
Tu						
We						
Th						
Fr						
Sa						
Su						
Weekly Goal						
Weekly Actual						
Year To Date						

this race the last several years.

	Swim	Bike	Run	Other
Su			AM: 45 min easy	Down from altitude
Mo			PM: 45 min easy	Travel to Kona, Hawaii
Tu	AM: 1 hour technique	PM: 2 hours easy		
We			PM: 2 hours up and down Hawi Hill. 1 hour 15 min easy, 4 x 1,000 m hard, 35 min easy	
Th	AM: i hour technique	1.5 hours easy fartlek		
Fr	The Test: 20 + 20 min swim in Kona Bay —> 3 hours bike —> 1 hour run (all hard)			
Sa	AM: 1.5 hours technique	PM: 1 hour easy		
Su			AM: w/u, 10 km Kona race at 150 BPM, w/d	PM: strength training with free weights
Mo	45 min technique	2 hours medium hard (~130 BPM)		
Tu	20 + 20 min in Kona Bay (85% of max)	1.5 hours easy fartlek		Massage
We			45 min (<145 BPM)	
Th	15 min easy	45 min easy		
Fr	Rest			

Table 12: Peaking for Hawaii in October

After 10 years and 24 Ironman races, Pauli has come to understand the value of recovery. He also feels that when you get older it may be difficult to do more than two Ironman races per year: "Don't overestimate your ability to recover from an Ironman distance race. You also have to handle the rest of your life."

Date/Day	Swim	Bike	Run			Notes
Mo						
Tu						
We						
Th						
Fr						
Sa						
Su						
Weekly Goal						
Weekly Actual						
Year To Date						

PAULA NEWBY-FRASER

A former ballet dancer and swimmer, Paula is the most famous of all female triathletes. She is a seven-time winner of the Hawaii Ironman and the only woman to break nine hours in Kona.

Paula originally outlined her present training methods in 1988. She obviously was way ahead of her time then: in that year's Hawaii Ironman, she was eleventh overall, and had an epic battle with the eventual tenth place finisher Pauli Kiuru, while dropping some of the best male athletes in the world. Though she has modified some of the elements of her training over the years, the basic structure remains: "My season starts January first and ends when I cross the finish line in Kona." She's got it figured out.

Paula's Long-Term Approach

To understand triathlons they way Paula does, consider the following:

- The triathlon is one activity, not three

- It is a sport of strength and endurance

- Everything revolves around key workouts

Three principles. So what? Many people still view the triathlon as consisting of three separate sports, or the duathlon as two. In fact, both the triathlon and the duathlon consist of one activity, but with three distinctly separate skills, or fundamentals. If you do a duathlon, you'll understand precisely. During the first run you can rely on speed; during the second, you have to rely on strength and endurance. Your training should be realistic enough to help you cope with these disparate loads and let you seamlessly connect the fundamentals into your one activity, the triathlon race.

Base Training

Paula's first couple of weeks are very easy. She gets her bike out of the bike bag in her garage (literally!), gathers her training gear, starts appearing at the weight room, swims a little on her own and runs a bit: "I'm preparing my system for exercise, that's all."

By mid to late January, she is ready to add some structure, which for her revolves around the key workouts: "My key workouts will build strength and endurance, I will add speed later. At this point, all my longer stuff is very slow, and slow by necessity." Her key workouts are in bold italics in Table 13 and are described further in the text below.

- *Monday swim:* A set of four to six 400s at 5:00 on 5:30.

- *The Tuesday Run:* A 12-mile partly hilly trail run for speed, strength and endurance; a sustained "hard/harder effort" type of run. Early on she'll join one of the slower groups and then work herself up as her fitness improves.

Weekly Focus: *Month & Year:*

Date/Day	Swim	Bike	Run			Notes
Mo						
Tu						
We						
Th						
Fr						
Sa						
Su						
Weekly Goal						
Weekly Actual						
Year To Date						

- *The Wednesday Ride:* A 70-mile ride, easy-and-friendly out and hard back.

- *Saturday:* An inland and partly mountainous bike ride alone or with friends: "I like to just hang out after the long bike ride, wash my car, go to the beach and enjoy myself. The evening jog is very easy, but important."

- *Sunday:* A steady paced hill run, approximately 13 miles long.

	Swim	Bike	Run	Other
Mo	*3,500 m*	1.5 - 2 hours	5 - 6 miles	
Tu	1,500 m easy		*AM: "Tuesday Run"* PM: 4 miles easy	Weights
We	3,000 m	*"Wednesday Ride"*	PM: 7 miles easy	
Th	1,500 m easy		1 hour steady hill run	Weights
Fr	3,000 m short intervals	2 hours easy	PM: 45 min easy	
Sa		*4 - 5 hours steady*	PM: 30 min easy	The Beach
Su	1,500 m easy		*1.5 hours steady*	Weights

Table 13: Paula's base training

Picking Up the Pace

Sometime in March, Paula has reached a steady state: "I like to feel fit, strong and able to cope with a heavier load by mid-March." She now modifies her base training by adding a second, slower recovery run on Thursday afternoon. Her Saturday ride is both harder and longer; up to six hours is not uncommon. The Sunday run is now two hours: "I'm fitter and everything's faster."

Racing Season

Weights go first—Paula feels that she has spent enough time working on muscle strength and now wants to focus on speed. While her run pick-ups a few months earlier may have been at a six-minute pace, she's now handling 5:30s with no problem. The overall distance is reduced: "By April first I start backing off from the long stuff; the big mileage weeks are now over. Hurrah!"

Her 120-mile ride is now 60 miles. The two hour run will now be one hour, but sometimes with a mile of hard pace in the middle. She is now riding 26 to 27 m.p.h. and running six-minute miles, as compared to the earlier 22 m.p.h. and seven-minute miles. She's down to a 1:10 for the Tuesday Run and the Wednesday Ride is harder: "Then I start racing." Now she'll do one hard (key) workout in each discipline per week and then the weekend race: "The weekends I don't race, I'll do a hard, hilly 45-mile ride followed

Date/Day	Swim	Bike	Run			Notes
Mo						
Tu						
We						
Th						
Fr						
Sa						
Su						
Weekly Goal						
Weekly Actual						
Year To Date						

by a five-mile transition run on Saturday and spend the whole afternoon on the beach."

	Swim	Bike	Run
Mo	*3,500 m*	1.5 - 2 hours	5 - 6 miles
Tu	1,500 m easy		*AM: shorter intervals* PM: 30 min easy
We	3,000 m	*45 - 60 miles hard*	PM: 7 miles easy
Th	1,500 m easy		1 hour steady hill run
Fr			30 min easy
Sa	(800 m easy)	30 min easy	30 min easy

Table 14: A training week before a Sunday race

Altitude Training in Boulder. In July and August, Paula goes to Boulder, Colorado to train at altitude. Here, and because she's also racing shorter distances, her long rides are 40 to 50 miles, and the long runs 10 to 12 miles. Instead of the Tuesday run, she does intervals on the track. "Part of the idea is to do something different. Boulder is almost like a vacation for me, I live with friends and don't have to deal with a house. It's great."

	Swim	Bike	Run	Other
Mo	3,500 m	1.5 hours easy	5 - 6 miles easy	"Get
Tu	1,500 easy	1.5 hours moderate	AM: "Tuesday Run" PM: 5 miles easy (optional)	a
We	3,000 m	"Wednesday Ride" + ~30 min	PM: 6 - 8 miles easy	tan
Th	1,500 m easy		AM: 1 hour steady hill run PM: 4 - 5 miles easy	for
Fr	1,000 m easy ocean	90+ miles steady	5 miles steady	the
Sa			2 - 2.5 hours steady	cameras
Su	1,500 m easy		1 hour very slow	in Kona"

Table 15: Paula's Hawaii Ironman training

The Ironman. By September, Paula is ready for the Hawaii Ironman. Her optimum preparation for this race, outlined in Table 15, is three weeks (yes, 3) of very specific training

Date/Day	Swim	Bike	Run			Notes
Mo						
Tu						
We						
Th						
Fr						
Sa						
Su						
Weekly Goal						
Weekly Actual						
Year To Date						

in San Diego. She is already fit; all she wants is to put the icing on the cake, to lose a little bit of body fat, to get lean and to peak, physically and mentally: "I see people consumed by the Ironman for months and months—they train themselves ridiculously, into this deep 'Valley of Fatigue' and just burn out, or get injured."

Paula takes the opposite approach. She wants to be on the upswing coming into Kona: "I normally stand on the Ironman starting line feeling that I could have done one more long ride and run."

Paula's Tapering and Peaking Secrets

Paula can take training very seriously. When necessary, she also emphasizes rest, particularly before a big race: "Absorb, absorb, absorb. Tapering is all about letting your body absorb all that hard training, and you certainly can't absorb while you're moving."

For the most important race of the year, Paula does a two-week taper and peak. She calls it her "14-day countdown." This period consists of physical, mental and nutritional preparations for each day, leaving nothing to chance. Also included is a mental check list of last-minute equipment details. She needs to know, for instance, that her shoes and racing gear won't chafe in combat. As an example, Table 16 summarizes what she's thinking of with 10 days to go (this chart is adapted from Paula's book *Peak Fitness for Women*, published by Human Kinetics in 1995).

Area	Notes
Physical	Train at a comfortable pace for 30 minutes. If you find these "easy" sessions boring, try a new route or work out with a group or club in your area.
Mental	You're just about one-third done in your mind's eye. You're feeling refreshed, taking pride in knowing you've finally made it this far in such great shape.
Nutrition	If you're having trouble digesting a high-carbohydrate diet and are experiencing gas spells, which is a common occurrence, try spacing out your meals in the day.
Other	If you've gotten your equipment, try it out on the road to make sure everything's in working order.

Table 16: Ten days before "The Big One"

She again emphasizes the importance of a good taper: "In the last two weeks before an endurance event like the Ironman, I have to keep reminding myself that nothing I do physically will make me go any faster on race day. It's what I have done four to five weeks ago that really determines my potential to have a strong race, not what I do four or five days before. The exercise of 'putting my feet up,' is the only thing that'll enable me to push a little harder."

Date/Day	Swim	Bike	Run			Notes
Mo						
Tu						
We						
Th						
Fr						
Sa						
Su						
Weekly Goal						
Weekly Actual						
Year To Date						

KAREN SMYERS

An individual medley and breaststroke swimmer in her youth and then at Princeton University, Karen got turned on by running as a form of pre-season training. Unheard of among swimmers in those days, she actually *liked* running and, over time, became an accomplished runner. She graduated with a B.A. in Economics and started working for a small consulting firm. In 1989, and after a 2:42 marathon PR, she decided to become a full-time professional triathlete: "I immediately jumped a level when I quit my job."

As a triathlete, she was known to excel at the short course races—she has six US National titles—but in 1993 she decided to give the Ironman a shot, ending up fourth in her first attempt. The year after, she came in second. And in 1995, she did the unthinkable, running down Paula Newby-Fraser with about half a mile to go, to win her first title in Kona. Five weeks later, she won the ITU World Triathlon Championship title.

She organizes her training similarly to the other top triathletes, while accounting for the climatic differences of her native Massachusetts. Living within a mile of Henry David Thoreau's Walden Pond, she frequently swims and runs there: "I actually run on the trails he would walk on to escape from the world and I did all of my long swims for the Ironman in the pond."

The Base Training

Karen starts making an effort to train more consistently in mid-January: "But if I have a five-day ski trip somewhere, I'm not going to worry about not swimming for five days." From March, through early May, she gradually builds her base, with a few high-intensity sessions: "I do some hard stuff, otherwise I would get bored. But I don't do as much volume as what I read other triathletes do; they must be adding 50 percent as a scare tactic."

One of her indoor workouts is a one-hour "pyramid session" on the turbo trainer, as outlined in Table 17. Most of her turbo training sessions are conducted with all her toys

Effort	Duration	Notes
Easy	15 min	While reading a book
Hard	X	X=1-2-3-4-5-4-3-2-1 minutes hard (focusing on cadence), interspersed by rest for half
Easy	0.5X	of the hard interval (focusing on recovery)
Easy	10-15 min	

Table 17: A pyramid on the turbo trainer

gathered around her: "Crucial to the success of this workout is to have real good 'psych-

Date/Day	Swim	Bike	Run			Notes
Mo						
Tu						
We						
Th						
Fr						
Sa						
Su						
Weekly Goal						
Weekly Actual						
Year To Date						

up' music. I like to listen to REM, Spin Doctors, Talking Heads and U2, and make up my own workout tapes." During the hard intervals, she likes to be down on the aerobars while focusing on form. On the shorter intervals, she'll use a harder gear and perhaps 80 RPM, while on the longer intervals, she'll change to a slightly easier gear and focus on keeping 100 RPM: "The in-between intervals are with in-between RPM. Sometimes, I'll work on leg speed and see if I can get up to 120, which is high for me. But the best thing about turbo training is that it's very concise. I don't like to waste a lot of time."

Up until a year ago, she never used a heart rate monitor. But after 10 years of training and racing, she has a very good sense of pace and effort: "I use 'perceived effort' and compare my workouts with how it would feel on the track."

The Pre-Competitive Season

Sometime in May she'll do a couple of races just to visit the "anaerobic domain" and to check how far her training has taken her: "After these races, I take a four- to five-week block of really good training to prepare myself for the season." Now she'll pay more attention to her hard workouts. She'll make sure to get in six key workouts—three bike and three run—every two weeks or so (shown in Table 18). Again, she uses her finely

Activity	Workout	Notes
Bike	Time trial	Either 10 miles or 2 by 5 miles with ~5 min rest
	Intervals	12 by 3 min hard with 2 min rest
	Hill repeats	4 hills, steep to gradual, each 1 to 2 min. She times every hill and does this four-hill sequence up to three times: "An unbelievable workout."
Run	On the track	3 by 1 mile, or 6 by half mile, or 12 by quarter mile
	"In and outs"	2 miles straight run, alternating quarters at 75 or 85 seconds for an average pace of, say, 5:20: "This makes you to dip into the 'anaerobics' and teaches your system to recover under stress. Great for learning pace."
	7 miles, tempo	1 mile warm-up, then a 5-mile loop at a steady 6-minute pace: "It's a great confidence builder." 1 mile warm down.

Table 18: Karen's key workouts during the pre-competitive season

tuned sense of perceived effort to compare her actual times—from both week to week and year to year—to gauge progress.

She feels that her organized swim workouts with the "Different Strokes" squad at the Boston City Hospital are sufficiently structured that she doesn't have to pay too much

Date/Day	Swim	Bike	Run			Notes
Mo						
Tu						
We						
Th						
Fr						
Sa						
Su						
Weekly Goal						
Weekly Actual						
Year To Date						

attention to them, just make sure she is there and ready to go.

The Transition from Short to Long Course

Now racing both short and long course, Karen has found the need for 80-mile rides throughout the early season; earlier in her career, she'd rarely ride more than 50. Her long runs are 13 miles, and she takes greater care not to skip them: "My longest run would be an hour; but during the short course season, I would sometimes slip. Now I try to do one longer run every week, unless I am racing two consecutive weekends. During my Ironman preparation, the long runs gradually increase to 20 miles."

Ideally, her Ironman-specific preparation (her key workouts are outlined in Table 19) is six weeks of focused training followed by a two-week taper and peak. However, the demands of short course racing sometimes force her to modify this schedule: "In 1995, I had to do three weeks of training, then one week of preparing for US Short Course Nationals, then three more weeks of training, then another short course race and then the two-week taper for Hawaii."

Day of Week	Workout	Karen's Comments
Wednesday's "Mini-Ironman"	Swim in Walden Pond: a 3,600 to 4,300 yards straight swim	"Learn the little things about a long swim; goggles may be too tight, etc."
	Ride: 50 to 60 miles with up to 2 by 30 min harder than Hawaii pace	"Learn to fuel up on the bike, using what you'll get on race day."
	Run: 10 to 13 miles at 6:30 pace, as the ultimate confidence builder	"Run efficiently fatigued, while absorbing what you take in."
Saturday's long bike to run	100-mile ride followed by an up to 5 mi transition run	"Focus on the ride and run until I get my legs back, then stop."
Sunday's long swim and run	15- to 20-mile run (6:50 pace) and 4,000 yard swim combination	"A steady aerobic run at slightly faster than my ideal Hawaii pace."

Table 19: Karen's key Ironman workouts

Diet and Nutrition

Rooming with short course specialist Gail Laurence before the 1995 World Championship in Mexico, she heard of Mike Garcia's dietary quote "I never met a calorie I didn't like," and proclaimed "that's me." In fact, she eats a well-rounded diet with plenty of complex carbohydrates, and red meat a couple of times per week. Because of a history of iron deficiency, she takes vitamins and minerals daily, particularly C, E and iron: "When I was running the marathon, I was listening to all the hype about how red meat is bad for you, and I got iron deficient. Now I try to be more balanced."

Date/Day	Swim	Bike	Run			Notes
Mo						
Tu						
We						
Th						
Fr						
Sa						
Su						
Weekly Goal						
Weekly Actual						
Year To Date						

Developing Your Own Schedule

With the information in this almanac, you are well equipped to develop your own work-outs to suit your personal schedule and objectives.

Seppo Nuuttila recommends that for races lasting less than three hours, the aerobic/anaerobic training ratio should be approximately 70/30. In other words, 70 percent of your weekly training should be aerobic. For races lasting more than four hours, the same ratio is 80/20. Table 20 shows how Seppo would coach two fictitious triathletes, Spencer, the short-course specialist and Paul, the long-course specialist. (Please note that any

Time of Year	Workout Type	Training Ratios [%]		Typical Blood Lactate Concentrations [mM]	
		Spencer	Paul	Spencer	Paul
Build-up	Aerobic	80	90	1-2	0.8-2
	Anaerobic	20	10	2-4	2-3
Pre-season	Aerobic	65	80	1-2	0.8-2
	Anaerobic	35	20	2-6	2-4
Competitive	Aerobic	60	75	1-2	0.8-2
	Anaerobic	40	25	2-10	2-5

Table 20: Spencer's and Paul's training ratios and lactate concentrations

resemblance to any triathlete, real or fictional, living or dead, is purely coincidental.)

In other words, if your focus is short course, you need to do more high intensity work-outs to teach your system to deal with lactic acid. If your focus is long course, you need to teach your body to use fat as a source of energy.

Remember that your body can deal with one form of training and improve for only so long. That's why all top triathletes adopt a multi-year "career plan" that cycles between aerobic base work, pre-competition training, competitive season and off season for the full calendar year. When the year is over, they get a new almanac, plan out the new year and do the same thing all over again. Performance = stress + rest.

Date/Day	Swim	Bike	Run			Notes
Mo						
Tu						
We						
Th						
Fr						
Sa						
Su						
Weekly Goal						
Weekly Actual						
Year To Date						

Appendix

Athlete: Jürgen Zäck
Race: 1995 Hawaii Ironman

In the chase for the lead pack 20 minutes into the bike

◀──

This appendix has a series of charts and templates to assist in documenting your training and racing experiences. Just remember, you don't have to fill out every box of every chart.

1. Training. The outline How to Personalize Your Almanac Log Page shows how some athletes are using the almanac. Then follows two Training Overview templates, the General with recommended training for the three phases described earlier, and the Personal for your own training. There are also three interval running charts with guidelines.

2. Interval training. These three pages allow you to summarize your interval workouts. You can use one each for the base training, pre-competitive and competitive seasons.

3. Strength training. These three pages allow you to summarize your strength workouts.

4. Annual training summary. The Annual Summary and Annual Chart grid allow you to summarize and plot distances or hours trained and other important data.

5. Goal setting. You can use the two Personal Best & Time Trial Record charts for your seasonal goal setting. There are two versions, Standard Distances and Favorite Distances. It is unlikely that you will fill both templates in a year's time.

6. Racing. There is one each of the Races To Do and Race Record templates.

7. Notes. For the more verbose among us are 12 empty notes pages with clever, inspirational or timely quotes.

8. Annual calendars. There are four annual calendars covering 1996 through 1999.

Please remember that all US and international copyright legislation apply. This means that you cannot, for instance, photocopy and distribute anything in this almanac.

How to Personalize Your Almanac Log Page

On the following page you will find several different ways to keep your log. Each day has a slightly different system, described below, none of which is significantly better than the other. You may, of course, be more or less detailed than some of these sample days. Keep it simple.

1 Monday. The day consisted of a 2,000 m swim, a 50 km bike ride and a 10 km run. The non-aerobic activities consisted of static active stretching (SAS) and one hour of strength training (weights).

2 Tuesday. This person likes to record the general feeling of health/wellness and uses a five-point scale where 1 is sick, 3 is good and 5 is great. Tuesday was a "good" day. After eight hours of sleep, the morning resting heart rate was 44 BPM, the morning weight was 70 kg. No training was recorded.

3 Wednesday. This athlete uses distances and an intensity scale of low, medium and high. The workouts were a 1,500 m swim at high intensity (85 to 100 percent of the MHR), a 30 km bike ride at medium intensity (70 to 85 percent) and a 5 km run at low intensity (55 to 70 percent), in no particular order. The other recordings are similar to Tuesday's athlete, but abbreviated. The day was "very good," the morning heart rate 40 BPM, the morning weight 80 kg, all after nine hours of sleep.

4 Thursday. This athlete is similar to Wednesday's, but uses a five-point scale of measuring intensity.

5 Friday. These entries are similar to the two above, but the athlete records hours trained rather than distances, as well intensities.

6 Saturday. This triathlete has recorded a four-hour transition (or combination) workout consisting of a one-hour swim, followed by a two-hour ride and a one-hour run (all at high intensities). The arrows between the swim, bike and run signify a transition workout, with no rest in between. This would probably be a time trial and would also be recorded on the personal best chart on page 144. Stretching in the afternoon.

7 Sunday. This is a really smart, though somewhat obsessed, triathlete.

About Week Numbering. In the upper right hand corner of the log page is room for the month and year. If you use the international weekly numbering system, you can put the number of the week in the month space. A triathlete from Sweden would probably put 34/97 for week 34 in 1997, or just 34.

Date/Day	Swim	Bike	Run	*Stretch*	*Weights*	Notes
1 Mo	2,000	50	10	SAS	1	
2 Tu Feel: 3 Pulse: 44 Weight: 70 Sleep: 8						
3 We F: 4 P: 40 W: 80 S: 9	1,500 H	30 M	5 L			
4 Th	1,500 4	30 3	5 2			
5 Fr	1.0 M	2.5 L	1.0 H			
6 Sa	1 —> H	2 —> H	1 H	SAS		*Four hour transition workout in moderate heat;* *great evening stretching session with Paula*
7 Su						*Day off, tired. Watched old Ironman tapes.*
Weekly Goal						
Weekly Actual						
Year To Date						

TRIATHLON TRAINING OVERVIEW—GENERAL

		Phase One	Phase Two	Phase Three
Objectives		Build confidence Learn skills	Differentiate training Increase intensity and volume	Further differentiation Improve skills Prepare for first race
Duration		4 weeks to 1 year	6 weeks to 6 months	6 weeks and on
Daily Training Range	**Metric** Swim	500 - 2,000	1,000 - 3,000	1,500 - 3,000
	Bike	15 - 40	25 - 60	40 - 120
	Run	3 - 12	6 - 15	8 - 25
	USA Swim	500 - 2,000	1,000 - 3,000	1,500 - 3,000
	Bike	10 - 25	15 - 40	25 - 75
	Run	2 - 8	4 - 10	5 - 15
Sessions/Week		6 - 8	7 - 9	10 - 12
Weekly Training Range	**Metric** Swim	2,000 - 4,000	4,000 - 6,000	8,000 - 12,000
	Bike	40 - 80	60 - 120	120 - 250
	Run	10 - 25	25 - 40	30 - 60
	USA Swim	2,000 - 4,000	4,000 - 6,000	8,000 - 12,000
	Bike	25 - 50	40 - 90	75 - 150
	Run	5 - 15	15 - 25	20 - 35
Comments		Add one session per week in your weakest event	4 days single workout 2 days double workout	2 - 3 days single workout 2 - 3 days double workout 1 day triple workout

TRIATHLON TRAINING OVERVIEW—PERSONAL

Objectives						
Duration						
Daily Training Range	Tri-ath-lon	Swim				
		Bike				
		Run				
	Other					
Sessions/Week						
Weekly Training Range	Tri-ath-lon	Swim				
		Bike				
		Run				
	Other					
Comments						

INTERVAL GUIDELINES

The traditional four variables of interval running are:

- distance
- run time
- recovery time
- number of repeats

On the next two pages are two interval training and pacing charts for an individual preparing to run a 10 kilometer foot race. The first one is based on the metric system and the second one on the mile (for some US athletes). The charts are provided for the more accomplished runner who would like to design his or her own interval workouts. They give approximate values for each of the above four variables based on your Actual Race Performance Time. **Please note that this is your *current* actual performance as opposed to your PR.**

Following these two charts is a summary of how to do intervals using your heart rate monitor.

INTERVAL RUNNING AND PACING—METRIC SYSTEM

Actual Race Performance			Training Interval Sessions								
Overall 10 km Time	Splits		2,000 m			1,000 m			400 m		
	km	400 m	Times		Number of Repeats	Times		Number of Repeats	Times		Number of Repeats
			Run	Recovery		Run	Recovery		Run	Recovery	
50:00	5:00	2:00	9:40-10:05	5 min	3	4:50-5:00	4 min	6	1:48-1:53	3 min	8
48:00	4:48	1:55	9:20-9:40	5 min	3	4:40-4:50	4 min	6	1:45-1:50	3 min	8
46:00	4:36	1:50	9:00-9:20	5 min	3	4:25-4:35	4 min	6	1:40-1:45	3 min	8
44:00	4:24	1:46	8:30-8:50	5 min	3-4	4:15-4:25	4 min	6	1:36-1:40	2 min	9
42:00	4:12	1:41	8:10-8:30	4 min	3-4	4:00-4:10	3 min	6	1:32-1:36	2 min	9
40:00	4:00	1:36	7:40-8:05	4 min	3-4	3:50-4:00	3 min	6-8	1:28-1:32	2 min	9
38:00	3:48	1:31	7:20-7:40	4 min	3-4	3:40-3:50	3 min	6-8	1:25-1:30	2 min	10
36:00	3:36	1:27	6:50-7:15	4 min	3-4	3:25-3:35	3 min	6-8	1:18-1:22	1.5 min	12
34:00	3:24	1:22	6:30-6:50	3 min	4-5	3:15-3:25	2 min	6-8	1:12-1:14	1.5 min	12
32:00	3:12	1:17	6:00-6:25	3 min	4-5	3:05-3:15	2 min	6-8	1:08-1:10	1.5 min	14
30:00	3:00	1:12	5:40-6:05	3 min	4-5	2:50-3:00	2 min	8-10	1:04-1:07	1 min	16
28:00	2:48	1:07	5:20-5:40	3 min	4-5	2:40-2:50	2 min	8-10	0.58-1:02	1 min	16

INTERVAL RUNNING AND PACING—US SYSTEM

Actual Race Performance			Training Interval Sessions								
Overall 10K Time	Splits		One Mile			Half Mile			Quarter Mile		
	Mile	Quarter Mile	Times		Number of Repeats	Times		Number of Repeats	Times		Number of Repeats
			Run	Recovery		Run	Recovery		Run	Recovery	
50:00	8:03	2:01	7:45-8:05	5 min	3	3:50-4:00	4 min	6	1:48-1:53	3 min	8
48:00	7:43	1:56	7:30-7:45	5 min	3	3:40-3:50	4 min	6	1:45-1:50	3 min	8
46:00	7:24	1:51	7:15-7:30	5 min	3	3:30-3:40	4 min	6	1:40-1:45	3 min	8
44:00	7:05	1:46	6:50-7:05	5 min	3-4	3:20-3:30	4 min	6	1:36-1:40	2 min	9
42:00	6:45	1:41	6:30-6:40	4 min	3-4	3:10-3:20	3 min	6	1:32-1:36	2 min	9
40:00	6:26	1:37	6:15-6:25	4 min	3-4	2:55-3:05	3 min	6-8	1:28-1:32	2 min	9
38:00	6:07	1:32	5:55-6:05	4 min	3-4	2:50-2:55	3 min	6-8	1:25-1:30	2 min	10
36:00	5:48	1:27	5:35-5:50	4 min	3-4	2:40-2:50	2 min	6-8	1:18-1:22	1.5 min	12
34:00	5:28	1:22	5:15-5:30	3 min	4-5	2:30-2:35	2 min	6-8	1:12-1:14	1.5 min	12
32:00	5:09	1:17	4:55-5:10	3 min	4-5	2:20-2:25	2 min	6-8	1:08-1:10	1.5 min	14
30:00	4:50	1:12	4:35-4:50	3 min	4-5	2:10-2:15	2 min	8-10	1:04-1:07	1 min	16
28:00	4:30	1:08	4:20-4:30	3 min	4-5	2:00-2:05	2 min	8-10	0.58-1:02	1 min	16

INTERVAL TRAINING USING A HEART RATE MONITOR

Access to a heart rate monitor invariably puts a new twist on interval training. Below are three heart rate based interval examples, one for circuit training[1] and two for running.

Time of Year	Activity	Distances / Repeats	Duration (seconds) On	Duration (seconds) Off	Heart Rates Maximum	Heart Rates Recovery	Notes
Base building	Circuit	3-6 rounds	30	30	Aerobic	Aerobic	
Base building	Running	6-8 x 1,000 m		120	AT	Aerobic	Recovery must be under aerobic threshold
Pre-competitive	Circuit	4-6 rounds	40	20	AT	Aerobic	
Pre-competitive	Running	6-8 x 1,000 m		90	AT	Aerobic	Recovery must be under aerobic threshold
Competitive	Circuit	4-6 rounds	50	10	>AT	AT	
Competitive	Running	6-8 x 1,000 m		60	>AT	Aerobic	Recovery must be under aerobic threshold
Any	"Pyramid Running"	5 x 2,000 m		60	Monitor your recovery heart rate. Ideally, the last recovery will be the same as the first. If it is, you are fit.		1st: under aerobic threshold 2nd: at aerobic threshold 3rd: between aerobic threshold and AT 4th: at AT 5th: under aerobic threshold

1. Circuit training is a series of strengthening exercises using your own body weight, free weights or resistance machines. For example, in the gym, you can do the following sequence: Bench Press –> Row –> Leg Curls –> Leg Extension –> Shoulder Press –> Lat Pull Downs –> Leg Press –> Biceps Curls –> Triceps Extensions –> Abdominals –> Obliques –> Back. You rest the indicated time between each exercise until the entire circuit is completed. Doing this circuit four to six times is a massive workout, even for the supremely fit.

INTERVAL TRAINING

Type/Set	Number of Repeats	Distance	Time	Interval or Recovery	Notes

INTERVAL TRAINING

Type/Set	Number of Repeats	Distance	Time	Interval or Recovery	Notes

INTERVAL TRAINING

Type/Set	Number of Repeats	Distance	Time	Interval or Recovery	Notes

STRENGTH TRAINING

Exercise	Set/Rep	Weight	Notes

STRENGTH TRAINING

Exercise	Set/Rep	Weight	Notes

STRENGTH TRAINING

Exercise	Set/Rep	Weight	Notes

ANNUAL TABLE

Week	Swim	Bike	Run	Notes		

Week	Swim	Bike	Run	Notes		
Total						

ANNUAL GRAPH

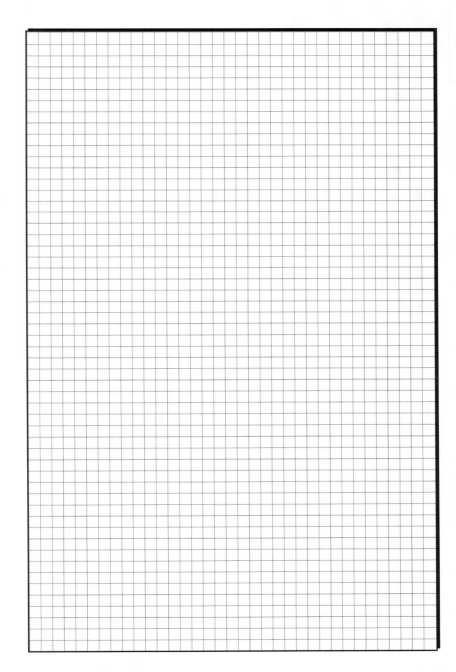

Note: Use this chart to plot your training values. In a bar chart, for instance, type of activity and intensity can be distinguished by using different colors and patterns. You may gain even more insight by correlating these graphic indicators with your weight, race results, feeling of well-being, and so on.

PERSONAL BEST & TIME TRIAL RECORD I

Standard Distances			All Time Personal Best		Base Building Period:		Pre-competitive Period:		Competitive Period:		Peaking Period:	
			Time	Date	Goal	Actual	Goal	Actual	Goal	Actual	Goal	Actual
Time Trials	Swim	100 m										
		500 m										
		1,500 m										
	Bike	16 km										
		40 km										
		100 km										
	Run	1,500 m										
		3 km										
		5 km										
		8 km										
Road Races		10 km										
		Half Marathon										
		Marathon										

Note: Although this is a grid of most meaningful time trial and racing distances, it is unlikely that you will fill out the entire chart in the course of a training and racing year.

PERSONAL BEST & TIME TRIAL RECORD II

Favorite Distances	All Time Personal Best		Base Building Period:		Pre-competitive Period:		Competitive Period:		Peaking Period:	
	Time	Date	Goal	Actual	Goal	Actual	Goal	Actual	Goal	Actual
Swim										
Bike										
Run										
Time Trials										

Note: Although this is a grid of most meaningful time trial and racing distances, it is unlikely that you will fill out the entire chart in the course of a training and racing year.

RACES TO DO

Date	Race	Location	Distances			Course Type	Goal	Prize Purse	Notes
			Swim	Bike	Run				

RACE RECORD

Date	Race	Location	Splits						Total Time	Place	Notes
			Swim	T1	Bike	T2	Run			

Notes

> *If you're not living on the edge you're taking up space.*
>
> Joel Kaplan
> ultrarunner

Notes

> *Success is what happens tomorrow.*
>
> Margaret Thatcher
> former Prime Minister
> of the United Kingdom

Notes

> *It's a long race, but it's catered.*
>
> Paul Huddle
> on the Hawaii Ironman

Notes

> When was the last time you did something for the first time?
>
> Sally Edwards
> athlete, author, motivator

Notes

> *If one advances confidently in the direction of his dreams, and endeavors to live the life which he has imagined, he will meet with the success unexpected in common hours.*
>
> Henry David Thoreau

Notes

> *When I'm afraid of losing, I never win.*
>
> Nick Campagna

Notes

> *In the long run, you hit only what you aim at.*
> *Therefore, though you should fail immediately,*
> *you had better aim at something high.*
>
> Henry David Thoreau

Notes

> *Looking back at my life seems like one long obstacle race with me as its chief obstacle.*
>
> Jack Paar

Notes

> *People are able to wonder at the height of huge mountains and the huge waves of the sea, the vast compass of the ocean, at the circular motion of the stars, and then pass by themselves without wondering at all.*
>
> Augustine

Notes

> *Women at the Ironman seem to have a better grasp of the Big Picture than the men.*
>
> Mike Plant

Notes

> *Waiting for waves is OK.*
> *Most people spend their lives waiting for*
> *nothing.*
>
> Unknown surfer

Notes

> *Imitators never get it right.*
>
> Tony Svensson

the total triathlon almanac
– 1993

the total triathlon almanac
second edition

PLANNING CALENDARS

1996

January	February	March	April
S M Tu W Th F S	S M Tu W Th F S	S M Tu W Th F S	S M Tu W Th F S
1 2 3 4 5 6	1 2 3	1 2	1 2 3 4 5 6
7 8 9 10 11 12 13	4 5 6 7 8 9 10	3 4 5 6 7 8 9	7 8 9 10 11 12 13
14 15 16 17 18 19 20	11 12 13 14 15 16 17	10 11 12 13 14 15 16	14 15 16 17 18 19 20
21 22 23 24 25 26 27	18 19 20 21 22 23 24	17 18 19 20 21 22 23	21 22 23 24 25 26 27
28 29 30 31	25 26 27 28 29	24 25 26 27 28 29 30	28 29 30
		31	

May	June	July	August
S M Tu W Th F S	S M Tu W Th F S	S M Tu W Th F S	S M Tu W Th F S
1 2 3 4	1	1 2 3 4 5 6	1 2 3
5 6 7 8 9 10 11	2 3 4 5 6 7 8	7 8 9 10 11 12 13	4 5 6 7 8 9 10
12 13 14 15 16 17 18	9 10 11 12 13 14 15	14 15 16 17 18 19 20	11 12 13 14 15 16 17
19 20 21 22 23 24 25	16 17 18 19 20 21 22	21 22 23 24 25 26 27	18 19 20 21 22 23 24
26 27 28 29 30 31	23 24 25 26 27 28 29	28 29 30 31	25 26 27 28 29 30 31
	30		

September	October	November	December
S M Tu W Th F S	S M Tu W Th F S	S M Tu W Th F S	S M Tu W Th F S
1 2 3 4 5 6 7	1 2 3 4 5	1 2	1 2 3 4 5 6 7
8 9 10 11 12 13 14	6 7 8 9 10 11 12	3 4 5 6 7 8 9	8 9 10 11 12 13 14
15 16 17 18 19 20 21	13 14 15 16 17 18 19	10 11 12 13 14 15 16	15 16 17 18 19 20 21
22 23 24 25 26 27 28	20 21 22 23 24 25 26	17 18 19 20 21 22 23	22 23 24 25 26 27 28
29 30	27 28 29 30 31	24 25 26 27 28 29 30	29 30 31

1997

January	February	March	April
S M Tu W Th F S	S M Tu W Th F S	S M Tu W Th F S	S M Tu W Th F S
1 2 3 4	1	1	1 2 3 4 5
5 6 7 8 9 10 11	2 3 4 5 6 7 8	2 3 4 5 6 7 8	6 7 8 9 10 11 12
12 13 14 15 16 17 18	9 10 11 12 13 14 15	9 10 11 12 13 14 15	13 14 15 16 17 18 19
19 20 21 22 23 24 25	16 17 18 19 20 21 22	16 17 18 19 20 21 22	20 21 22 23 24 25 26
26 27 28 29 30 31	23 24 25 26 27 28	23 24 25 26 27 28 29	27 28 29 30
		30 31	

May	June	July	August
S M Tu W Th F S	S M Tu W Th F S	S M Tu W Th F S	S M Tu W Th F S
1 2 3	1 2 3 4 5 6 7	1 2 3 4 5	1 2
4 5 6 7 8 9 10	8 9 10 11 12 13 14	6 7 8 9 10 11 12	3 4 5 6 7 8 9
11 12 13 14 15 16 17	15 16 17 18 19 20 21	13 14 15 16 17 18 19	10 11 12 13 14 15 16
18 19 20 21 22 23 24	22 23 24 25 26 27 28	20 21 22 23 24 25 26	17 18 19 20 21 22 23
25 26 27 28 29 30 31	29 30	27 28 29 30 31	24 25 26 27 28 29 30
			31

September	October	November	December
S M Tu W Th F S	S M Tu W Th F S	S M Tu W Th F S	S M Tu W Th F S
1 2 3 4 5 6	1 2 3 4	1	1 2 3 4 5 6
7 8 9 10 11 12 13	5 6 7 8 9 10 11	2 3 4 5 6 7 8	7 8 9 10 11 12 13
14 15 16 17 18 19 20	12 13 14 15 16 17 18	9 10 11 12 13 14 15	14 15 16 17 18 19 20
21 22 23 24 25 26 27	19 20 21 22 23 24 25	16 17 18 19 20 21 22	21 22 23 24 25 26 27
28 29 30	26 27 28 29 30 31	23 24 25 26 27 28 29	28 29 30 31
		30	

PLANNING CALENDARS

1998

January
S	M	Tu	W	Th	F	S
				1	2	3
4	5	6	7	8	9	10
11	12	13	14	15	16	17
18	19	20	21	22	23	24
25	26	27	28	29	30	31

February
S	M	Tu	W	Th	F	S
1	2	3	4	5	6	7
8	9	10	11	12	13	14
15	16	17	18	19	20	21
22	23	24	25	26	27	28

March
S	M	Tu	W	Th	F	S
1	2	3	4	5	6	7
8	9	10	11	12	13	14
15	16	17	18	19	20	21
22	23	24	25	26	27	28
29	30	31				

April
S	M	Tu	W	Th	F	S
			1	2	3	4
5	6	7	8	9	10	11
12	13	14	15	16	17	18
19	20	21	22	23	24	25
26	27	28	29	30		

May
S	M	Tu	W	Th	F	S
					1	2
3	4	5	6	7	8	9
10	11	12	13	14	15	16
17	18	19	20	21	22	23
24	25	26	27	28	29	30
31						

June
S	M	Tu	W	Th	F	S
	1	2	3	4	5	6
7	8	9	10	11	12	13
14	15	16	17	18	19	20
21	22	23	24	25	26	27
28	29	30				

July
S	M	Tu	W	Th	F	S
			1	2	3	4
5	6	7	8	9	10	11
12	13	14	15	16	17	18
19	20	21	22	23	24	25
26	27	28	29	30	31	

August
S	M	Tu	W	Th	F	S
						1
2	3	4	5	6	7	8
9	10	11	12	13	14	15
16	17	18	19	20	21	22
23	24	25	26	27	28	29
30	31					

September
S	M	Tu	W	Th	F	S
		1	2	3	4	5
6	7	8	9	10	11	12
13	14	15	16	17	18	19
20	21	22	23	24	25	26
27	28	29	30			

October
S	M	Tu	W	Th	F	S
				1	2	3
4	5	6	7	8	9	10
11	12	13	14	15	16	17
18	19	20	21	22	23	24
25	26	27	28	29	30	31

November
S	M	Tu	W	Th	F	S
1	2	3	4	5	6	7
8	9	10	11	12	13	14
15	16	17	18	19	20	21
22	23	24	25	26	27	28
29	30					

December
S	M	Tu	W	Th	F	S
		1	2	3	4	5
6	7	8	9	10	11	12
13	14	15	16	17	18	19
20	21	22	23	24	25	26
27	28	29	30	31		

1999

January
S	M	Tu	W	Th	F	S
					1	2
3	4	5	6	7	8	9
10	11	12	13	14	15	16
17	18	19	20	21	22	23
24	25	26	27	28	29	30
31						

February
S	M	Tu	W	Th	F	S
	1	2	3	4	5	6
7	8	9	10	11	12	13
14	15	16	17	18	19	20
21	22	23	24	25	26	27
28						

March
S	M	Tu	W	Th	F	S
	1	2	3	4	5	6
7	8	9	10	11	12	13
14	15	16	17	18	19	20
21	22	23	24	25	26	27
28	29	30	31			

April
S	M	Tu	W	Th	F	S
				1	2	3
4	5	6	7	8	9	10
11	12	13	14	15	16	17
18	19	20	21	22	23	24
25	26	27	28	29	30	

May
S	M	Tu	W	Th	F	S
						1
2	3	4	5	6	7	8
9	10	11	12	13	14	15
16	17	18	19	20	21	22
23	24	25	26	27	28	29
30	31					

June
S	M	Tu	W	Th	F	S
		1	2	3	4	5
6	7	8	9	10	11	12
13	14	15	16	17	18	19
20	21	22	23	24	25	26
27	28	29	30			

July
S	M	Tu	W	Th	F	S
				1	2	3
4	5	6	7	8	9	10
11	12	13	14	15	16	17
18	19	20	21	22	23	24
25	26	27	28	29	30	31

August
S	M	Tu	W	Th	F	S
1	2	3	4	5	6	7
8	9	10	11	12	13	14
15	16	17	18	19	20	21
22	23	24	25	26	27	28
29	30	31				

September
S	M	Tu	W	Th	F	S
			1	2	3	4
5	6	7	8	9	10	11
12	13	14	15	16	17	18
19	20	21	22	23	24	25
26	27	28	29	30		

October
S	M	Tu	W	Th	F	S
					1	2
3	4	5	6	7	8	9
10	11	12	13	14	15	16
17	18	19	20	21	22	23
24	25	26	27	28	29	30
31						

November
S	M	Tu	W	Th	F	S
	1	2	3	4	5	6
7	8	9	10	11	12	13
14	15	16	17	18	19	20
21	22	23	24	25	26	27
28	29	30				

December
S	M	Tu	W	Th	F	S
			1	2	3	4
5	6	7	8	9	10	11
12	13	14	15	16	17	18
19	20	21	22	23	24	25
26	27	28	29	30	31	

ORDER FORM

Trimarket
2264 Bowdoin Street
Palo Alto, CA 94306
USA

Phone: 1-415-494-1406
Fax: 1-415-494-1413

In the US, call toll free:
1-800-533-3644

International orders please submit an inter-national money order drawn on a US bank.

Please send me the following:

_____ each of Can You Make a Living Doing That? by Brad Kearns at $9.95

_____ each of Scott Tinley's finding the wheel's hub at $9.95

_____ each of the total runner's almanac at $12.95

_____ each of the total fitness log at $9.95

_____ each of the total triathlon almanac - 3 *(third edition)* at $16.95

_____ each of the total triathlon almanac *(second edition)* at $16.95

_____ each of the total triathlon almanac - 1993 *(first edition)* at $16.95

Special: all three editions of the total triathlon almanac (including priority shipping within the USA) at $45.00

_____ each of the video Strength Training for Total Body Fitness by Mark Allen and Paula Newby-Fraser with certified fitness specialist Diane Buchta at $29.95

In California, add 7.75% sales tax

Shipping, within USA $3.00 ($1.00 each additional)

Shipping, priority (or international) $5.00 ($2.00 each additional)

TOTAL _____

I understand that I may return any unused book for a full refund if not satisfied.

Name: _____

Address: _____

New

finding the wheel's hub
by Scott Tinley

One of triathlon's enduring legends, this Ironman Hall of Famer tells it all in this his third book. Described by running's Bill Rodgers as, quote: "Scott Tinley brings you into the intense eye of the triathlon, spelling it out clearly and with a potent sense of humor. I found this a fascinating book."

$9.95

New

Can You Make a Living Doing That?
by Brad Kearns

Mark Allen describes this book as, quote: "a refreshing departure from the common 'how to' books in sports. Brad goes beyond the race results and workout miles to provide an intimate look at the lifestyle of a professional athlete. I highly recommend this book from one of the most colorful personalities in sports today."

$9.95

New

the total fitness log

this new multifitness book has advice from top fitness authorities. Includes sections on:

- cycling
- running
- walking
- nutrition
- swimming
- cross-training
- in-line skating
- mountain biking
- working out in the gym
- training with a heart rate monitor

$9.95

the total runner's almanac

is, like the total triathlon almanacs, a comprehensive logbook and training manual, but for the runner. Described by UK *Runner's World Magazine* as, quote: "the Rolls Royce of training diaries [and] If you can only afford one running book this year, make it this one — it's worth it."

Our best-selling book.

$12.95

Order form on reverse page